PERFECT PUZZLES

CROSSWORD

hinkler

hinkler

Published by Hinkler Pty Ltd
45–55 Fairchild Street
Heatherton Victoria 3202 Australia
www.hinkler.com.au

Puzzles © Clarity Media 2022
Design: Hinkler Studio
Images © Shutterstock.com

ISBN: 978 1 4889 2446 0

Printed and bound in China

PUZZLES

CROSSWORD **1**

1/29/2023
Brooklynne

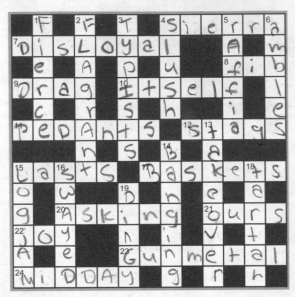

	F		F		T		S	i	e	r	r	a
D	i	s	L	O	y	a	l				A	m
	e		A		p		u			f	i	b
D	r	a	g		I	t	s	e	l	f		l
	c		r		s		h			i		e
P	e	D	A	n	t	s		S	t	a	g	s
			n		s		B	a				
L	a	s	t	s		B	a	s	k	e	t	s
O		w			D		n	e			a	
g		A	s	k	i	n	g		O	u	r	s
J	O	y			n		i		v		t	
A		e			G	u	n	m	e	t	a	l
M	i	D	D	A	Y		g		r		h	

Across

4 Long mountain chain (6)
7 Unfaithful (8)
8 Lie (3)
9 Haul (4)
10 Stifle (anag.) (6)
11 People who insist on sticking to formal rules (7)
12 Bucks (5)
15 Endures (5)
17 Containers (7)
20 Putting a question to (6)
21 Belonging to us (4)
22 Happiness (3)
23 Alloy of copper and tin (8)
24 Noon (6)

Down

1 Violent in force (6)
2 Obviously offensive (of an action) (8)
3 Computer keyboard users (7)
4 Partly melted snow (5)
5 A palm tree (6)
6 Walks slowly (6)
13 Assume control of (4,4)
14 Knocking loudly (7)
15 Situation that appears irresolvable (6)
16 Moved back and forth (6)
18 Fabric associated with Scotland (6)
19 Drab (5)

1/29/2023
Brooklynne

CROSSWORD 2

Across

1 Device that regulates water flow (8)
5 Con; swindle (4)
9 Unabridged (5)
10 Public passenger-carrying vehicle (7)
11 Focused light beam (5)
12 Tree (3)
13 Danger (5)
15 Relaxed; not tense (5)
17 Appropriate (3)
19 Record on tape (5)
20 Japanese warrior (7)
21 Winged animals (5)
22 Finishes (4)
23 A lament (8)

Down

1 Spicy fish stew (13)
2 Migratory grasshoppers (7)
3 Butterfly larvae (12)
4 Less warm (6)
6 Venomous snake (5)
7 Naughtily (13)
8 Hard to fathom (12)
14 Endure (7)
16 Aloof (6)
18 Domesticated (5)

CROSSWORD 3

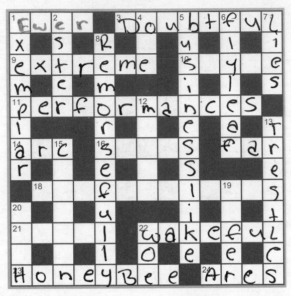

Across

1 Pitcher (4)
3 Uncertain (8)
9 Exceptional; not usual (7)
10 Manner of speaking (5)
11 Renditions (12)
14 Part of a curve (3)
16 Basins (5)
17 Distant (3)
18 Tricky elements; obstacles (12)
21 Bits of meat of low value (5)
22 Sleepless (7)
23 Social insect (8)
24 Greek god of war (4)

Down

1 Thing serving as an appropriate model (8)
2 Organic compound (5)
4 Be in debt (3)
5 Efficient (12)
6 Blank page in a book (7)
7 Falsehoods (4)
8 Regretfully (12)
12 Frenzied (5)
13 Settlers (anag.) (8)
15 Light fabric often made of silk (7)
19 Conclude (5)
20 Luxurious (4)
22 Great distress (3)

CROSSWORD 4

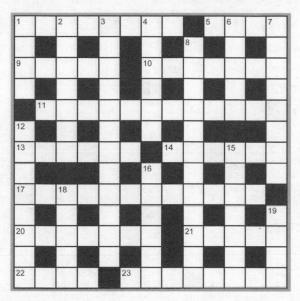

Across

1 Official document (8)
5 Musical composition (4)
9 Sudden forward thrust (5)
10 Make damp (7)
11 Part of the mind (12)
13 Legume (6)
14 Hire for work (6)
17 Amiable (4-8)
20 Acted properly (7)
21 Domestic cat (5)
22 Currency of France and Germany (4)
23 Worrying problem (8)

Down

1 Long and thin piece of wood (4)
2 Reddening of the skin (7)
3 Dictatorial (12)
4 Manors (anag.) (6)
6 Paved courtyard (5)
7 Ominous (8)
8 Unhappy (12)
12 Qualified for entry (8)
15 Sour in taste (7)
16 Smear or blur (6)
18 Opposite one of two (5)
19 Computer memory unit (4)

CROSSWORD 5

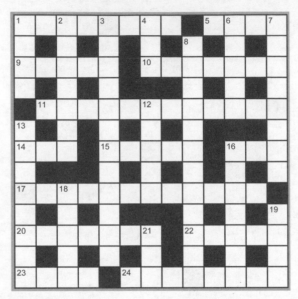

Across

1 Come before in time (8)
5 Moved through water (4)
9 Main artery (5)
10 Not limited to one class (7)
11 In a greedy manner (12)
14 Flower that is not yet open (3)
15 Possessor (5)
16 Pasture; meadow (3)
17 Inflexible (12)
20 Unlawful (7)
22 Short high-pitched tone (5)
23 Core meaning (4)
24 Peacemaker (8)

Down

1 Expression of regret (4)
2 Prospered (7)
3 Ability to see the future (12)
4 Excavated soil (3)
6 Merchandise (5)
7 Our galaxy (5,3)
8 Incurably bad (12)
12 Ice cream is often served in these (5)
13 Accommodating (8)
16 Surgical knives (7)
18 Stories (5)
19 Strong pole on a ship (4)
21 Surpass (3)

CROSSWORD 6

Across

1 Carry on with (8)
5 Type of light (4)
8 Things to be done (5)
9 Wild (of an animal) (7)
10 Cornmeal (7)
12 Agrees or corresponds (7)
14 State of lawlessness (7)
16 Close group (7)
18 Kettledrums (7)
19 U-shaped curve in a river (5)
20 Fathers (4)
21 Gauges (8)

Down

1 Pretty (4)
2 Capital of The Bahamas (6)
3 Determined; not allowing refusal (9)
4 Takes the place of (6)
6 Equipping with weapons (6)
7 Chiropody (8)
11 Places (9)
12 Taught (8)
13 Added together (6)
14 Reach a destination (6)
15 Arched shape of a road (6)
17 Pairs (4)

CROSSWORD 7

Across

1 Nitrous oxide (8,3)
9 Faint southern constellation (5)
10 Chewy substance (3)
11 Device that splits light (5)
12 Wading bird (5)
13 Squeezes (8)
16 Wedge to keep an entrance open (8)
18 Measures duration (5)
21 Mark of insertion (5)
22 Cereal plant (3)
23 Not together (5)
24 Coordinate (11)

Down

2 Reached a destination (7)
3 Novelty (7)
4 Cause to start burning (6)
5 Chart (5)
6 Ire (5)
7 Belief something will happen (11)
8 Freed (11)
14 Farm vehicle (7)
15 Faintly illuminated at night (7)
17 Church instruments (6)
19 Move as fast as possible (5)
20 Reduce prices substantially (5)

CROSSWORD 8

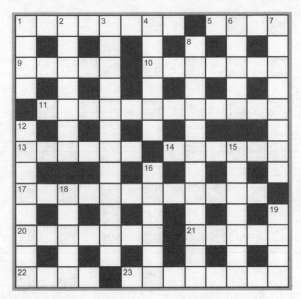

Across

1 Walks unsteadily (8)
5 Young sheep (4)
9 Tiny piece of food (5)
10 Surplus or excess (7)
11 Having a tendency to become
liquid (12)
13 Solemn promise (6)
14 Elegant and slender (6)
17 Quarrelsome and
uncooperative (12)
20 The first Gospel (7)
21 Female relation (5)
22 Prying; overly curious (4)
23 Apprehended (8)

Down

1 Unwell (4)
2 Four-stringed guitar (7)
3 List of books referred to (12)
4 Exit; Bible book (6)
6 With speed (5)
7 Inhaled (8)
8 Persistence (12)
12 Astronaut (8)
15 Noisiest (7)
16 Long pin (6)
18 Short letters (5)
19 Unwanted wild plant (4)

CROSSWORD 9

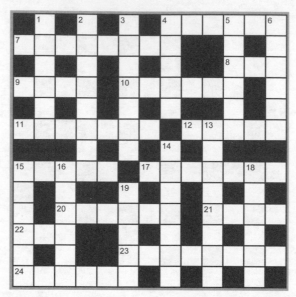

Across

4 Deprive of force (6)
7 Rodent (8)
8 Possess (3)
9 Country in South America (4)
10 Embarrassing mistake (3-3)
11 Spiral cavity of the inner ear (7)
12 Enthusiasm (5)
15 Board game (5)
17 Visually appealing (7)
20 Decide with authority (6)
21 Military unit (4)
22 Epoch (3)
23 Mammal with a sticky tongue (8)
24 Abandon (6)

Down

1 Lively Spanish dance (6)
2 Lays in wait for (8)
3 Muttered (7)
4 Evil spirit (5)
5 Dribbles (6)
6 Papal representative (6)
13 Commotion (8)
14 Reroutes (7)
15 Unfounded story (6)
16 Small shrubs with pithy stems (6)
18 Marine gastropod (6)
19 Special reward (5)

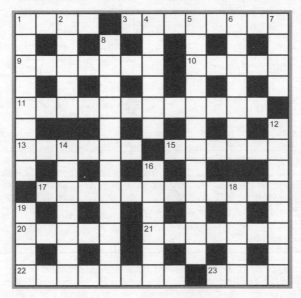

Across

1 Has to (4)
3 Done away with (8)
9 Repudiated (7)
10 Type of herring (5)
11 Displeased (12)
13 Geneva (anag.) (6)
15 Bubble violently (6)
17 The proprietor of an eating establishment (12)
20 Rejuvenate (5)
21 Compels (7)
22 Narrow street or passage (8)
23 Killer whale (4)

Down

1 Circle of constant longitude (8)
2 Puts through a sieve (5)
4 Small parrot (informal) (6)
5 Intolerable (12)
6 Strong stream of water (7)
7 Dark brown oval fruit (4)
8 Immediately (12)
12 State of the USA (8)
14 Endless (7)
16 Atmospheric phenomenon (6)
18 Edward ___ : English composer (5)
19 Song for a solo voice (4)

CROSSWORD 11

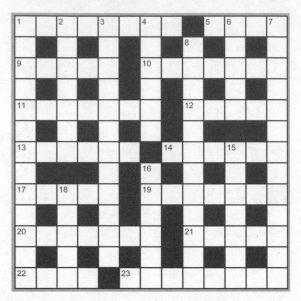

Across

1 Anniversary of when you are born (8)
5 Desert in central China (4)
9 E.g. taste or touch (5)
10 Lock of curly hair (7)
11 Very young infant (7)
12 Higher in place (5)
13 Exclusively (6)
14 Undoes (6)
17 Cry of excitement (5)
19 Stations at the ends of routes (7)
20 Drink containing vermouth (7)
21 Come with (5)
22 Facial feature (4)
23 Reassign (8)

Down

1 Female professional (13)
2 Regeneration (7)
3 Written in pictorial symbols (12)
4 Exposing one's views (6)
6 Spring flower (5)
7 Fascinatingly (13)
8 Immune (12)
15 Existing at the beginning (7)
16 Conflict or struggle (6)
18 Unpleasant giants (5)

CROSSWORD 12

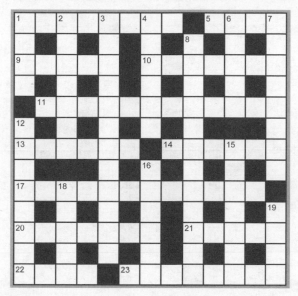

Across

1 Reserved in advance (3,5)
5 Goad on (4)
9 Porcelain (5)
10 Proportionately (3,4)
11 Contests (12)
13 Sculptured symbols (6)
14 Urges to do something (6)
17 Explanatory section of a book (12)
20 Floating mass of frozen water (7)
21 Leaves out (5)
22 Smug (anag.) (4)
23 Gusty (8)

Down

1 Draw into the mouth using a straw (4)
2 Group of three plays (7)
3 Marksman (12)
4 Person who acts for another (6)
6 Musical instrument (5)
7 Re-evaluate (8)
8 Scornful (12)
12 Setting fire to (8)
15 Passionate (7)
16 Club (6)
18 Unit of heat (5)
19 Catch sight of (4)

CROSSWORD 13

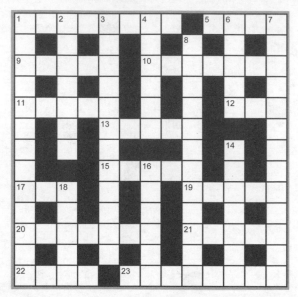

Across

1 Personal magnetism (8)
5 Extremities of the feet (4)
9 Damp (5)
10 Actually; in reality (2,5)
11 Rope with a running noose (5)
12 Inform upon (3)
13 Put off (5)
15 Fabric (5)
17 Pen point (3)
19 Woodwind instruments (5)
20 Country in northern Africa (7)
21 Third Greek letter (5)
22 Part of an egg (4)
23 Settling (anag.) (8)

Down

1 Acting to complete a whole (13)
2 Assumed identities (7)
3 Preliminary (12)
4 Free from ostentation (6)
6 Academy award (5)
7 Meteors (8,5)
8 An idea that is added later (12)
14 Ice statues with coal for eyes (7)
16 Elaborately adorned (6)
18 Ring-shaped roll (5)

CROSSWORD 14

Across

1 Pertaining to marriage (11)
9 Second planet from the sun (5)
10 Athletic facility (3)
11 Form of oxygen (5)
12 Iron alloy (5)
13 Provoking (8)
16 Opera texts (8)
18 Crime of setting something on fire (5)
21 Ticked over (of an engine) (5)
22 Come together (3)
23 Regions (5)
24 Thinking about (11)

Down

2 Prompting device (7)
3 Returns to a former state (7)
4 Minor official (6)
5 Birds lay their eggs in these (5)
6 Tiny aquatic plants (5)
7 Cheat someone financially (5-6)
8 Petty (5-6)
14 Large fast warship (7)
15 Rich white cheese (7)
17 Have as a purpose (6)
19 Group of gunshots (5)
20 Approaches (5)

CROSSWORD 15

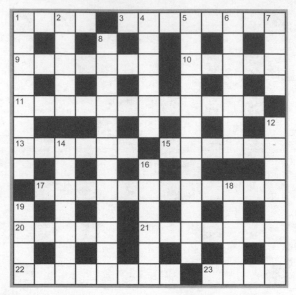

Across

1 Implement for styling hair (4)
3 Rubbed with the hands (8)
9 Concepts (7)
10 Smells strongly (5)
11 Understandably (12)
13 Thick innermost digits (6)
15 Nasal (6)
17 Intuitively designed (of a system) (4-8)
20 Thorax (5)
21 Type of diving (4-3)
22 The whole of something (8)
23 Chef (4)

Down

1 Is composed of (8)
2 Short choral composition (5)
4 Attack (6)
5 Starting here (anag.) (12)
6 Imaginary mischievous sprite (7)
7 Stage of twilight (4)
8 Fellow plotter (12)
12 Listen to again (4,4)
14 Brushed off the face (of hair) (7)
16 Approval; recognition (6)
18 Dance club (5)
19 Spots (4)

CROSSWORD 16

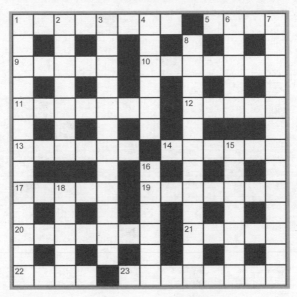

Across

1 Deadlock (5-3)
5 Performs on stage (4)
9 Expressing emotions (of poetry) (5)
10 Impresario (7)
11 Reticular (7)
12 Person who flies an aircraft (5)
13 One of the halogens (6)
14 Large wine bottle (6)
17 Fault (5)
19 Ship worker (7)
20 Affluent (7)
21 Ballroom dance (5)
22 Moved quickly (4)
23 Uses again (8)

Down

1 Magnificent (13)
2 Introduced air to (7)
3 Lexicons (12)
4 Seeks information indirectly (6)
6 Humped ruminant (5)
7 Holier-than-thou (13)
8 In a self-satisfied manner (12)
15 Existing solely in name (7)
16 Attack with severe criticism (6)
18 Awake from slumber (5)

CROSSWORD 17

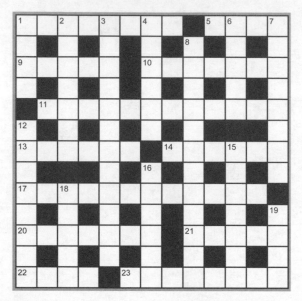

Across

1 Took in (8)
5 Garden outbuilding (4)
9 Ring solemnly (5)
10 Moving to and fro (7)
11 Explanatory (12)
13 Not ready to eat (of fruit) (6)
14 Small carnivorous mammal (6)
17 Type of cloud (12)
20 Insanitary (7)
21 River cove; bay (5)
22 Long bounding stride (4)
23 Conclusive argument (8)

Down

1 Sink (anag.) (4)
2 Better for the environment (7)
3 Working for oneself (4-8)
4 Continent (6)
6 Port-au-Prince is the capital here (5)
7 Obstinately (8)
8 Rate of increase in speed (12)
12 Prompt (8)
15 Make a sucking sound (7)
16 Not written in any key (of music) (6)
18 Repeat something once more (5)
19 Agitate (4)

Across

1 Charged particles (4)
3 Support at the top of a seat (8)
9 Increase the duration of (7)
10 Country in the Middle East (5)
11 Cereal plant (3)
12 Distinguishing character (5)
13 Faithful (5)
15 Piece of furniture (5)
17 Half of six (5)
18 Metric unit of measurement (historical) (3)
19 Beast (5)
20 Sweet icing (7)
21 Decorated with a raised design (8)
22 Wet with condensation (4)

Down

1 Very subtle (13)
2 Loop with a running knot (5)
4 Fourscore (6)
5 Doubting the truth of (12)
6 Terrestrial (7)
7 Party lanterns (anag.) (13)
8 Entirety (12)
14 Agitate (7)
16 Confuse (6)
18 Saying (5)

CROSSWORD 19

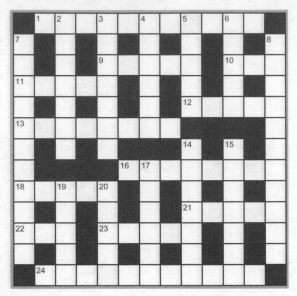

Across

1 Person who looks identical to another (6,5)
9 Attach (5)
10 Type of vase (3)
11 Darkness (5)
12 Moist stiff mixture (5)
13 Tidiness (8)
16 Secured; tied (8)
18 Arrive at (5)
21 Decorate (5)
22 Religious sister (3)
23 Timer (anag.) (5)
24 Stargazers (11)

Down

2 Licentious (7)
3 Wandering (7)
4 Alludes to (6)
5 Confusion (3-2)
6 Sticks together (5)
7 Contriving to bring about (11)
8 Act of going before in time (11)
14 Layer or band of rock (7)
15 Reveal (7)
17 Keen insight (6)
19 Female relatives (5)
20 Employer (5)

CROSSWORD 20

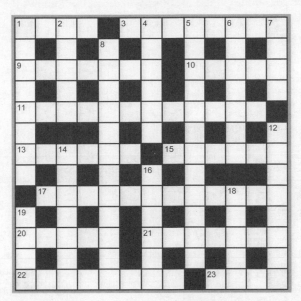

Across

1 Method; fashion (4)
3 Beating (8)
9 Loaning (7)
10 Force upon (5)
11 Shrewdness (12)
13 Neat and concise; irritable (6)
15 Claw (6)
17 Donation (12)
20 Polite address for a woman (5)
21 Combined metals (7)
22 Move out the way of (8)
23 Large deer (pl.) (4)

Down

1 Distance marker in a race (8)
2 Benefactor (5)
4 Amount of money left in a will (6)
5 Contagiously (12)
6 Stupid (7)
7 Movable barrier (4)
8 Thick-skinned herbivorous animal (12)
12 Explosive shells (8)
14 Evaded (7)
16 Widen (6)
18 Pastoral poem (5)
19 Mischievous sprites (4)

CROSSWORD 21

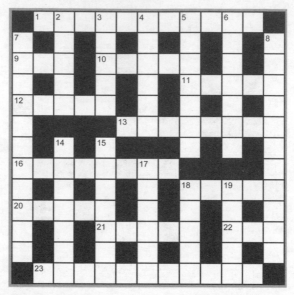

Across

1 For all practical purposes (11)
9 Range of knowledge (3)
10 Complete; absolute (5)
11 Creator (5)
12 Parts (anag.) (5)
13 Person engaging in a complicated dispute (8)
16 Troublemaker (8)
18 Wild animal; monster (5)
20 Act of going in (5)
21 Gets less difficult (5)
22 Large passenger-carrying vehicle (3)
23 Celebrity (11)

Down

2 More delicate (5)
3 Supply with; furnish (5)
4 Unsteady gait (6)
5 State of the USA (7)
6 Fortunately (7)
7 Very tall buildings (11)
8 Type of artist (11)
14 Painting; photograph (7)
15 Legal practitioners (7)
17 Prayer (6)
18 Aromatic herb (5)
19 Head monk of an abbey (5)

CROSSWORD 22

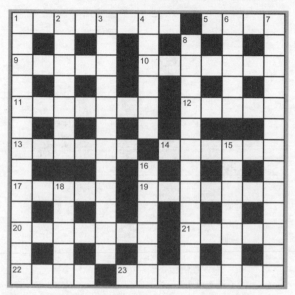

Across

1 Tempting (8)
5 Heavenly body (4)
9 Connection; link (3-2)
10 European country (7)
11 Commander in chief of a fleet (7)
12 Command (5)
13 Recount; narrate (6)
14 Person to whom a lease is granted (6)
17 Drive forward (5)
19 Use again (7)
20 Sterile (7)
21 Words that identify things (5)
22 Legendary creature (4)
23 Gathering (8)

Down

1 Noteworthy and rare (13)
2 Relating to heat (7)
3 Pay tribute to another (12)
4 Take small bites out of (6)
6 Three-note chord (5)
7 Pitilessly (13)
8 Fence closure (anag.) (12)
15 Give in to temptation (7)
16 Short written works (6)
18 Tailored fold (5)

CROSSWORD 23

Across

1 Hard shell of a crustacean (8)
5 Block a decision (4)
9 African country whose capital is Niamey (5)
10 Imply as a condition (7)
11 Musical speeds (5)
12 Ate (anag.) (3)
13 Seat (5)
15 Lawful (5)
17 Entirely (3)
19 High up (5)
20 Sudden inclination to act (7)
21 A leaf of paper (5)
22 Invalid; void (4)
23 Official orders (8)

Down

1 Group of stars (13)
2 Ways of doing things (7)
3 Especially (12)
4 Stout-bodied insect (6)
6 Crumble (5)
7 Excessively striving (13)
8 Inadequately manned (12)
14 Pamphlet (7)
16 Photographic equipment (6)
18 Folded-back part of a coat (5)

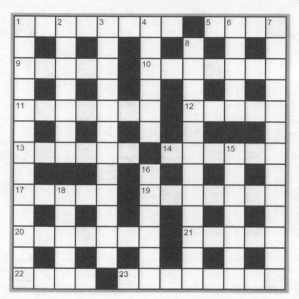

Across

1 Reasoning logically (8)
5 Cook (4)
9 Pretend (5)
10 Country in northern Africa (7)
11 Backtrack (7)
12 Household garbage (5)
13 Scratch (6)
14 Quantity (6)
17 Prophet (5)
19 End result (7)
20 Blanked (7)
21 Outstanding (of a debt) (5)
22 Require (4)
23 Shape of the waxing moon (8)

Down

1 Removal of trees from an area (13)
2 Wanderer (7)
3 Characteristic of the present (12)
4 Write a music score (6)
6 Plantain lily (5)
7 Boxing class division (13)
8 Directions (12)
15 Dark red halogen (7)
16 Boundary (6)
18 Spirit in a bottle (5)

CROSSWORD 25

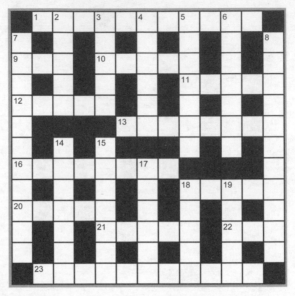

Across

1 Astronomer who studies the origin of the universe (11)
9 Piece of cloth (3)
10 Woody-stemmed plant (5)
11 Punctuation mark (5)
12 Singing voice (5)
13 Rain tree (anag.) (8)
16 Substitutes (8)
18 Moneys owed (5)
20 Solemn promises (5)
21 Bird sound (5)
22 Goal (3)
23 Attention-grabbing (3-8)

Down

2 Church instrument (5)
3 District council head (5)
4 Find (6)
5 Icy (7)
6 One of several parts (7)
7 Community with a common interest (11)
8 Argumentative (11)
14 The growth of crystals (7)
15 Harsh; corrosive (7)
17 Special ___ : film illusion (6)
18 Trench (5)
19 Muscular strength (5)

CROSSWORD **26**

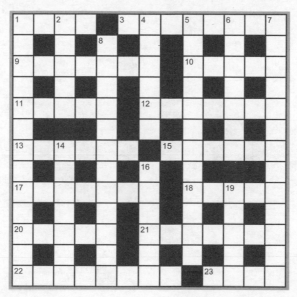

Across

1 Crack (4)
3 Emphasis (anag.) (8)
9 Perils (7)
10 Settle for sleep (of birds) (5)
11 Small antelope (5)
12 Small-scale model (7)
13 Item of neckwear (6)
15 Long-haired variety of cat (6)
17 Irreverence (7)
18 Asian country (5)
20 Golf clubs (5)
21 Topmost (7)
22 Longing (8)
23 Prestigious TV award (4)

Down

1 Property of elements with unstable nuclei (13)
2 What a mycologist studies (5)
4 Situated within the confines of (6)
5 Environment (12)
6 Pear-shaped fruit native to Mexico (7)
7 Wastefully; lavishly (13)
8 Food shop (12)
14 Ancient large storage jar (7)
16 Punctuation mark (6)
19 You usually do this while asleep (5)

CROSSWORD 27

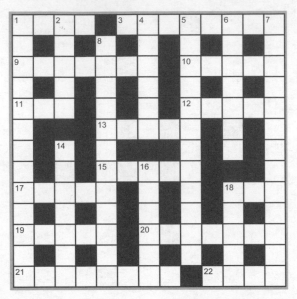

Across

1 Closed hand (4)
3 Intelligentsia (8)
9 Jumping (7)
10 Poisonous (5)
11 Tree of the genus Quercus (3)
12 Positive electrode (5)
13 Silk fabric (5)
15 Wash with water (5)
17 Wireless (5)
18 Sound of a cow (3)
19 Individual things (5)
20 Pays no attention to (7)
21 Moving at speed (8)
22 Fill or satiate (4)

Down

1 Continue a stroke in tennis (6,7)
2 Flash of light (5)
4 Take into the body (of food) (6)
5 Separation; alienation (12)
6 Worried and nervous (7)
7 Recoils unduly (anag.) (13)
8 Ruinously (12)
14 Dirtier (7)
16 Concept (6)
18 Wall painting (5)

CROSSWORD 28

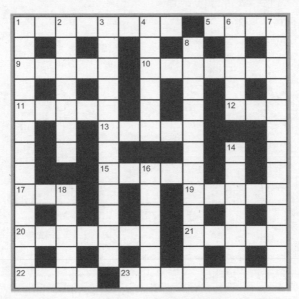

Across

1 Not appropriate (8)
5 Pace (4)
9 Make law (5)
10 Tortilla rolled around a filling (7)
11 Songbird (5)
12 17th Greek letter (3)
13 Fits of violent anger (5)
15 Sense experience (5)
17 Slippery fish (3)
19 Lover of Juliet (5)
20 Grotesque monster (7)
21 Former name of Myanmar (5)
22 Canines (4)
23 Person granted a permit (8)

Down

1 Wet behind the ears (13)
2 Portable enclosure for infants (7)
3 Fully extended (12)
4 Flowing back (6)
6 One who always puts in a lot of effort (5)
7 Corresponding (13)
8 Capable of being moved (12)
14 Photographic devices (7)
16 Type of seasoned sausage (6)
18 Reclining (5)

CROSSWORD 29

Across

1 Price (4)
3 Squid (8)
9 Becomes fully grown (7)
10 Secret rendezvous (5)
11 Sap (anag.) (3)
12 Brazilian dance (5)
13 First appearance (5)
15 Good sense (5)
17 Male aristocrat (5)
18 Food item from a hen (3)
19 Strong gust of wind (5)
20 Marine mammal (7)
21 All people (8)
22 Land measure (4)

Down

1 Friendly (13)
2 Stomach exercise (3-2)
4 Soak up (6)
5 Creatively (12)
6 Terrible (7)
7 Inflexibility (13)
8 Deceitfully (12)
14 Clasp (7)
16 Aureate (6)
18 Principle of morality (5)

CROSSWORD 30

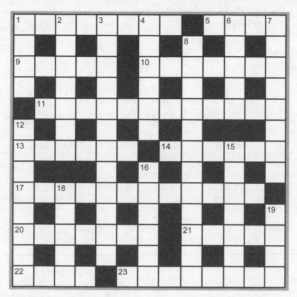

Across

1 Sorcerer (8)
5 Mineral powder (4)
9 Sweeping implement (5)
10 Rower (7)
11 Detective (12)
13 Mischievous (6)
14 Recreate (6)
17 Having keen vision (5-7)
20 Series of boat races (7)
21 Inapt (anag.) (5)
22 Told an untruth (4)
23 Person of varied learning (8)

Down

1 Gangs (4)
2 Adult (5-2)
3 Corresponding; proportionate (12)
4 Long-legged rodent (6)
6 Confess to be true (5)
7 Pet birds (8)
8 Reckless; ready to react violently (7-5)
12 Relating to deep feelings (8)
15 United States (7)
16 Fierce woman (6)
18 Large bird of prey (5)
19 State of the USA (4)

CROSSWORD 31

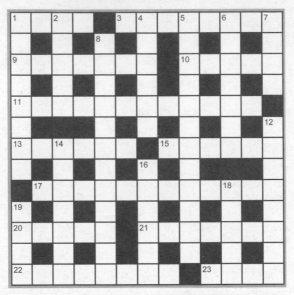

Across

1 Red gem (4)
3 Straw hat (8)
9 Humorous drawing (7)
10 Needing to be scratched (5)
11 Private (12)
13 Make beloved (6)
15 Small cave (6)
17 Separately (12)
20 Obtain information from various sources (5)
21 Quick musical tempo (7)
22 Settles (8)
23 Arduous journey (4)

Down

1 Rebound (8)
2 Element with atomic number 5 (5)
4 16 of these in a pound (6)
5 In an energetic manner (12)
6 Bewitch (7)
7 Semi-precious agate (4)
8 Inspiring action (12)
12 Exterior of a motor vehicle (8)
14 Domestic beasts of burden (7)
16 Countenance (6)
18 Beer (5)
19 Gelatinous substance (4)

CROSSWORD 32

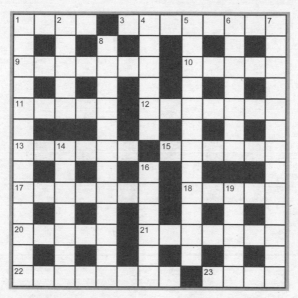

Across

1 Decays (4)
3 Give someone the courage to do something (8)
9 Chanted (7)
10 E.g. Pacific or Atlantic (5)
11 Comedian (5)
12 Pamphlet (7)
13 Expressing regret (6)
15 Compel by intimidation (6)
17 Formally approved (7)
18 Lubricated (5)
20 Form of expression (5)
21 Fabled monster (7)
22 Refer to famous people one knows (4-4)
23 Ancient harp (4)

Down

1 Rebirth in a new body (13)
2 ___ pole: tribal emblem (5)
4 Self-contained unit (6)
5 Use of words that mimic sounds (12)
6 Inhabitant (7)
7 Absence (13)
8 Not familiar with or used to (12)
14 Selfishness (7)
16 In slow tempo (of music) (6)
19 Towering (5)

CROSSWORD 33

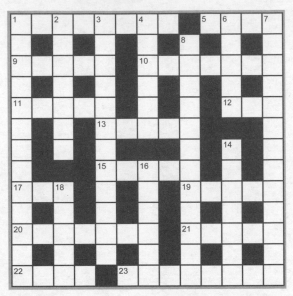

Across

1 Took a firm stand (8)
5 Matured (4)
9 Sag (5)
10 Slanted characters (7)
11 Clergyman (5)
12 Touch gently (3)
13 Requirements (5)
15 Tall structure on a castle (5)
17 What a painter creates (3)
19 Semiaquatic mammal (5)
20 Country whose capital is Reykjavik (7)
21 Spike used by a climber (5)
22 Wooden crosspiece attached to animals (4)
23 Extremely lovable (8)

Down

1 Originality (13)
2 Uncomplaining (7)
3 Occult (12)
4 Fit for consumption (6)
6 Remorse (5)
7 Act of vanishing (13)
8 Person who listens in to conversations (12)
14 Water container (7)
16 Removed unwanted plants (6)
18 Pinch; squeeze (5)

Across

1 Result (11)
9 Staple food (5)
10 Adult males (3)
11 Stead (anag.) (5)
12 Smarter (5)
13 Not curly (of hair) (8)
16 Expression of gratitude (5,3)
18 Up and about (5)
21 Refrain from (5)
22 High ball in tennis (3)
23 Distinctive design (5)
24 Oppressed (11)

Down

2 Public speakers (7)
3 Layer of earth (7)
4 Extinguish (a fire) (6)
5 Equip (5)
6 Temporary lodgings (5)
7 Not wanted (11)
8 Unwilling to believe (11)
14 Breathed in sharply (7)
15 Cause to absorb water (7)
17 Factory siren (6)
19 Avoided by social custom (5)
20 From the capital of Italy (5)

CROSSWORD 35

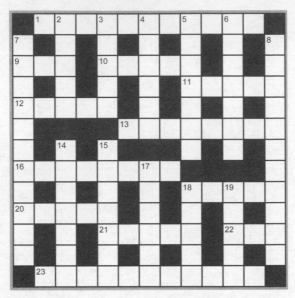

Across

1 Clay pottery (11)
9 Wild ox (3)
10 First Pope (5)
11 Royal (5)
12 Scraped at (5)
13 Mounted guns (8)
16 Last (8)
18 Sea duck (5)
20 Come to a point (5)
21 Should (5)
22 Before the present (3)
23 Designed for usefulness (11)

Down

2 Twisted to one side (5)
3 Lukewarm (5)
4 Book of the Bible (6)
5 Writ for an arrest (7)
6 Fixing; manipulating (7)
7 Compassionate (11)
8 Impenetrable (11)
14 Fragment (7)
15 Entangle (7)
17 Small in degree (6)
18 Consumer (5)
19 Stage play (5)

Across

1 Repeated jazz phrase (4)
3 Go beyond a limit (8)
9 Greedy drinker (7)
10 Spree (5)
11 Attempt to do (3)
12 In a slow tempo (of music) (5)
13 Strange and mysterious (5)
15 Capital of Japan (5)
17 Aqualung (5)
18 Fluffy scarf (3)
19 Bring to the conscious mind (5)
20 Cunning (7)
21 Most saccharine (8)
22 Openly refuse to obey an order (4)

Down

1 Virtuousness (13)
2 Bubbly (5)
4 Church official (6)
5 Troublemaker (6-6)
6 Outburst of anger (7)
7 Principally (13)
8 First part of the Bible (3,9)
14 Simple sugar (7)
16 Locks lips with (6)
18 Brass instrument (5)

CROSSWORD 37

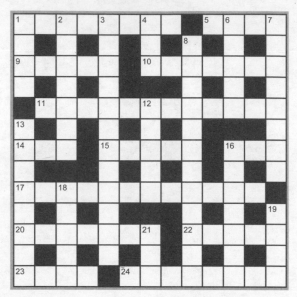

Across

1 Salad sauce (8)
5 Ostrich-like bird (4)
9 Pertaining to the voice (5)
10 Retirement income (7)
11 Laudatory (12)
14 Louse egg (3)
15 Outdo (5)
16 One's family (3)
17 Flaw (12)
20 Mass of flowers (7)
22 Seawater (5)
23 Female sheep (pl.) (4)
24 Chord played in rapid succession (8)

Down

1 Jump into water (4)
2 Extract (7)
3 Narcissism (4-8)
4 Bite sharply (3)
6 Robbery (5)
7 Irritating (8)
8 Contradictory (12)
12 Composition for a solo instrument (5)
13 Arousing jealousy (8)
16 Done in full awareness (7)
18 Lying flat (5)
19 Brave person; idol (4)
21 Ram (anag.) (3)

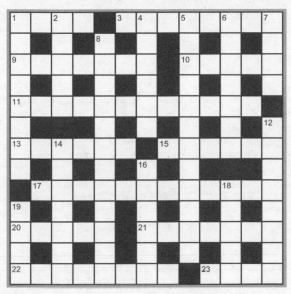

Across

1 Fair (4)
3 Absurd (8)
9 Cherubic (7)
10 Burrowing animals (5)
11 Ate excessively (12)
13 Waterlogged areas of ground (6)
15 Remove from a container (6)
17 Extremely large (12)
20 About (5)
21 Accommodation (7)
22 Medicine (8)
23 Lots (anag.) (4)

Down

1 Envy (8)
2 Smooth transition (5)
4 Assent or agree to (6)
5 Dark towering cloud (12)
6 Volcanic crater (7)
7 Girl or young woman (4)
8 Crucial (3-9)
12 Window in a roof (8)
14 Distant runner-up in a horse race (4-3)
16 Heavy metal weight used by a ship (6)
18 Cool down (5)
19 Short tail (4)

CROSSWORD 39

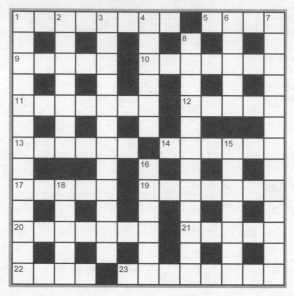

Across

1 Signal (8)
5 Particles around a comet (4)
9 Free from dirt (5)
10 Saying (7)
11 Powerful dog (7)
12 Burst of light (5)
13 Small insect (6)
14 Expedition to see animals (6)
17 Do really well at (5)
19 Decaying organic matter (7)
20 One who holds property for another (7)
21 Game of chance (5)
22 System of contemplation (4)
23 Opposites (8)

Down

1 Ineptly (13)
2 Piece of furniture (7)
3 Friendliness (12)
4 Inside information (3-3)
6 Dramatic musical work (5)
7 Shortened forms of words (13)
8 Not catching fire easily (12)
15 Quantities (7)
16 Partition that divides a room (6)
18 Held on to something tightly (5)

CROSSWORD 40

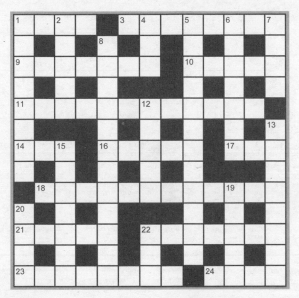

Across

1 Free from doubt (4)
3 Verifying (8)
9 Put in order (7)
10 Destitute (5)
11 Knowledge of a future event (12)
14 Short sleep (3)
16 Fortune-telling card (5)
17 Broken equipment (3)
18 Conjectural (12)
21 Eighth Greek letter (5)
22 Person who keeps watch (7)
23 Grumbled (8)
24 Feeling of resentment or jealousy (4)

Down

1 Losing grip (8)
2 Natural elevation (5)
4 Removed from sight (3)
5 Person's physical state (12)
6 Freezing (3-4)
7 Men (4)
8 Exorbitant (12)
12 Compass point (5)
13 Great adulation (8)
15 Remittance (7)
19 Headgear of a monarch (5)
20 Plant stalk (4)
22 Sheltered side (3)

CROSSWORD 41

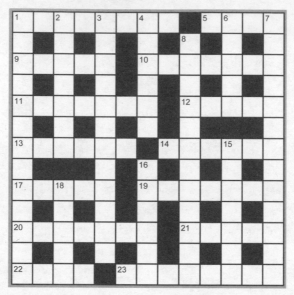

Across

1 Crucial (8)
5 Familiar name for a potato (4)
9 Swift (5)
10 Refiles (anag.) (7)
11 Collection of sheets of paper (7)
12 Purchaser (5)
13 Failing to win (6)
14 Entices to do something (6)
17 Move effortlessly through air (5)
19 River in Africa (7)
20 Part of a church near the altar (7)
21 Employing (5)
22 Welsh emblem (4)
23 Paternal (8)

Down

1 Arranged in temporal order (13)
2 Momentum (7)
3 Freedom from control (12)
4 Wear away (6)
6 Reverence for God (5)
7 Upsettingly (13)
8 Gossip (12)
15 First in importance (7)
16 Deciduous flowering shrub (6)
18 Lacking meaning (5)

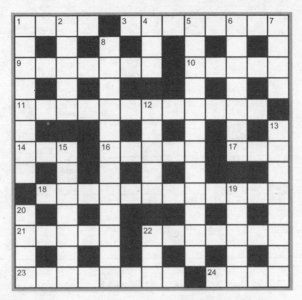

Across

1 Standard (4)
3 Put forward an idea (8)
9 This evening (7)
10 Proposal of marriage; bid (5)
11 Style of piano-based blues (6-6)
14 Top (anag.) (3)
16 Beneath (5)
17 Acquire; obtain (3)
18 Metal device for removing tops (6,6)
21 Lucid (5)
22 Respire (7)
23 Holding close (8)
24 Cut of beef from the leg (4)

Down

1 Laptop (8)
2 Musical form with a recurrent theme (5)
4 Degenerate (3)
5 Cameraperson (12)
6 Sorting through (7)
7 Mend with rows of stitches (4)
8 Relating to farming (12)
12 Chunk (5)
13 Large fish (8)
15 Gardening tools (7)
19 Indentation (5)
20 Examine quickly (4)
22 Disallow (3)

CROSSWORD 43

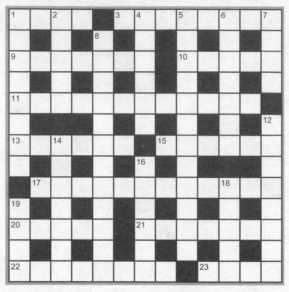

Across

1 Travel by horse (4)
3 Gift of money (8)
9 Flight hub (7)
10 Humiliate (5)
11 Blasphemous (12)
13 Blush (6)
15 Starlike object that often emits radio waves (6)
17 Valetudinarianism (12)
20 Dens (5)
21 Beating (7)
22 Commonplace (8)
23 Sort; variety (4)

Down

1 Restore confidence to (8)
2 Style of Greek architecture (5)
4 Song of devotion (6)
5 Courtesy (12)
6 Sculptured figures (7)
7 Seek (anag.) (4)
8 Vehemently (12)
12 Three-sided figure (8)
14 Period between sunrise and sunset (7)
16 Irrational fear (6)
18 Showery (5)
19 Sheet of floating ice (4)

CROSSWORD 44

Across

1 Amazes (8)
5 Modify (4)
9 Chocolate powder (5)
10 Fabric (7)
11 Individual things (5)
12 Title of a married woman (3)
13 Extreme (5)
15 Cake decoration (5)
17 Bath vessel (3)
19 Turf out (5)
20 Rotate (7)
21 Stringed instrument (5)
22 Bell-shaped flower (4)
23 Participant in a meeting (8)

Down

1 Pertaining to building design (13)
2 Permits to travel (7)
3 Modestly (12)
4 Hate (6)
6 Belief in a god or gods (5)
7 Hidden store of valuables (8,5)
8 Capable of being traded (12)
14 Ruled (7)
16 Purpose (6)
18 Tool for marking angles (5)

CROSSWORD 45

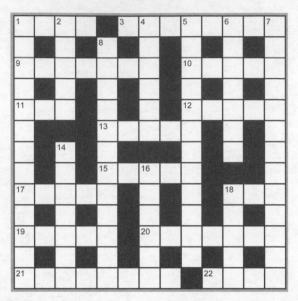

Across

1 Ill-mannered (4)
3 Precise and clear (8)
9 Primarily (7)
10 Bring together (5)
11 Deep hole in the ground (3)
12 Faith in another (5)
13 Firearm (5)
15 Sweet-scented shrub (5)
17 Run away with a lover (5)
18 Popular beverage (3)
19 Modifies (5)
20 Victory (7)
21 Showering with liquid (8)
22 Fly high (4)

Down

1 Open-mindedness (13)
2 Believer in a supreme being (5)
4 Bribe (6)
5 Comical tuner (anag.) (12)
6 Lack of success (7)
7 Code-breaker (13)
8 Easily (12)
14 More spacious (7)
16 Subatomic particle such as an electron (6)
18 Speed music is played at (5)

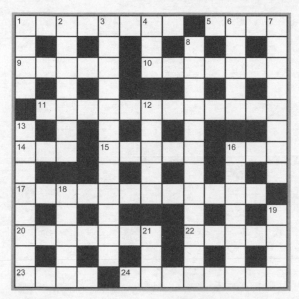

Across

1 Incorporates (8)
5 Imitated (4)
9 Prize (5)
10 Shelters for dogs (7)
11 Someone who sets up their own business (12)
14 Popular edible fish (3)
15 Supply with new weapons (5)
16 Secret retreat (3)
17 Ugly (12)
20 Yearbook (7)
22 Senior figure in a tribe (5)
23 Main body of a book (4)
24 Discard; abandon (8)

Down

1 Tehran is the capital here (4)
2 Linked together (7)
3 Insuring (12)
4 Large deer (3)
6 Annoy (5)
7 Wishing for (8)
8 Sporadic (12)
12 Public square (5)
13 Resident (8)
16 Separates into parts (7)
18 Mingle with something else (5)
19 Smile broadly (4)
21 Stimulus (3)

CROSSWORD 47

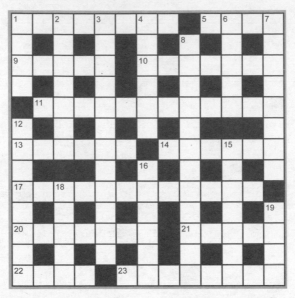

Across

1 Midwestern US state (8)
5 Gemstone (4)
9 Embarrass (5)
10 Flightless seabird (7)
11 Easy to converse with (12)
13 Wireless communication devices (6)
14 Written in verse (6)
17 Not intoxicating (of a drink) (12)
20 Frozen water spears (7)
21 Willow twig (5)
22 Increased in size (4)
23 Two-wheeled vehicles (8)

Down

1 Average value (4)
2 Impressed a pattern on (7)
3 Dreamy; odd and unfamiliar (12)
4 Revoke (6)
6 Ball of lead (5)
7 Clemency (8)
8 Study of human societies (12)
12 Imbibing (8)
15 Insignificant (7)
16 Art of growing dwarfed trees (6)
18 Sound (5)
19 Ancient boats (4)

CROSSWORD 48

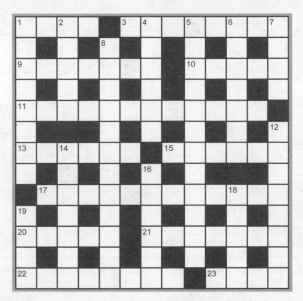

Across

1 Source of inspiration (4)
3 Magician (8)
9 Bodies of writing (7)
10 Take illegally (5)
11 Total destruction (12)
13 Innate (6)
15 Serious situation (6)
17 Without parallel (6,2,4)
20 Chopping (5)
21 Sets fire to (7)
22 Floating masses of frozen water (8)
23 Weapons (4)

Down

1 Person who repairs cars (8)
2 Sound of an emergency vehicle (5)
4 Mouthpiece of the gods (6)
5 Compensate for (12)
6 Loud and hoarse (7)
7 Engrossed (4)
8 First language (6,6)
12 Judges; evaluates (8)
14 Straight line between two places (7)
16 Doing nothing (6)
18 External (5)
19 Country where one finds Bamako (4)

CROSSWORD 49

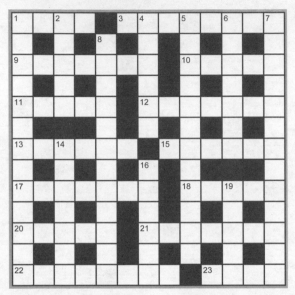

Across

1 Fastening mechanism (4)
3 Capital of Australia (8)
9 Made of clay hardened by heat (7)
10 Gush out in a jet (5)
11 Coral reef (5)
12 Sum added to interest (7)
13 Seem (6)
15 Bear witness (6)
17 Electronic retention of data (7)
18 Relating to a city (5)
20 Breed of dog (5)
21 Domestic implement (7)
22 Ant email (anag.) (8)
23 Hard to make out; indistinct (4)

Down

1 Lazy (13)
2 Freight (5)
4 Consider to be true (6)
5 Wearing glasses (12)
6 Procedure; standard (7)
7 In a reflex manner (13)
8 Process of combining (12)
14 Schedule of activities (7)
16 Take away (6)
19 Pleasing view (5)

CROSSWORD 50

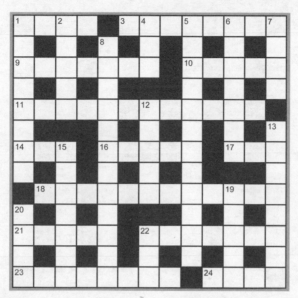

Across

- **1** Centre (4)
- **3** Glass-like volcanic rock (8)
- **9** Scare rigid (7)
- **10** Out of fashion (5)
- **11** Framework for washed garments (12)
- **14** Exclamation of contempt (3)
- **16** Home (5)
- **17** Cry (3)
- **18** Boxing class division (12)
- **21** Protective garment (5)
- **22** Silhouette (7)
- **23** Curative medicines (8)
- **24** Preparation for Easter (4)

Down

- **1** Maximum number a stadium can hold (8)
- **2** Imitative of the past (5)
- **4** Broad inlet of the sea (3)
- **5** Enhancements (12)
- **6** Demands forcefully (7)
- **7** Christmas (4)
- **8** Dispirited (12)
- **12** Search rigorously for (5)
- **13** Point of contact; masonry support (8)
- **15** A general proposition (7)
- **19** Steer (5)
- **20** Couple (4)
- **22** Material from which metal is extracted (3)

CROSSWORD 51

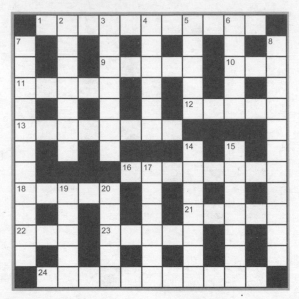

Across

1 Easy target (7,4)
9 Daisy-like flower (5)
10 Lyric poem (3)
11 Friends (5)
12 Device used to connect to the internet (5)
13 Wrongdoings (8)
16 Unyielding (8)
18 Recently (5)
21 Raise up (5)
22 Tree of the genus Ulmus (3)
23 Makes a garment from wool (5)
24 Incalculable (11)

Down

2 Legal inquiry (7)
3 Kitchen appliance (7)
4 Acquired money as profit (6)
5 Kind of wheat (5)
6 Spoke softly (5)
7 Escorted (11)
8 Opposite of temporarily (11)
14 Shrub with tubular flowers (7)
15 Pertaining to matrimony (7)
17 Minimal bathing suit (6)
19 Ladies (5)
20 Bonds of union (5)

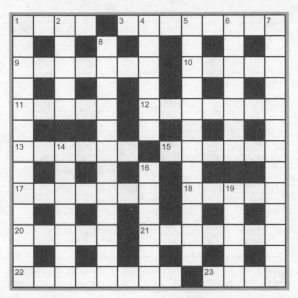

Across

1 Dubs (anag.) (4)
3 Well-rounded (8)
9 Design style of the 1920s and 1930s (3,4)
10 Appear suddenly (3,2)
11 Titled (5)
12 Feeling of vexation (7)
13 Calamitous (6)
15 Treeless Arctic region (6)
17 Flower-shaped competition award (7)
18 Boredom (5)
20 Angry (5)
21 Dry red table wine of Italy (7)
22 Mobster (8)
23 Dairy product (4)

Down

1 Group problem-solving technique (13)
2 Piece of information (5)
4 Admit openly (6)
5 Using letters and numbers (12)
6 Skipped about (7)
7 Reliability (13)
8 Female school boss (12)
14 Refrain from (7)
16 Free from danger (6)
19 A number between an eighth and a tenth (5)

CROSSWORD 53

Across

1 Affiliation (11)
9 Make a living with difficulty (3)
10 Hankered after (5)
11 Bore into (5)
12 Join together as one (5)
13 Revolted (8)
16 Perceived (8)
18 Intended (5)
20 Not concealed (5)
21 Mythical monster (5)
22 Commotion (3)
23 Basically (11)

Down

2 Lance (5)
3 Egg-shaped (5)
4 Exist permanently in (6)
5 A child beginning to walk (7)
6 Small bone (7)
7 Branch of medicine dealing with skin disorders (11)
8 Curse (11)
14 Upward slopes (7)
15 Hard but fragile (7)
17 Send for sale overseas (6)
18 Mediterranean island country (5)
19 Use to one's advantage (5)

CROSSWORD **54**

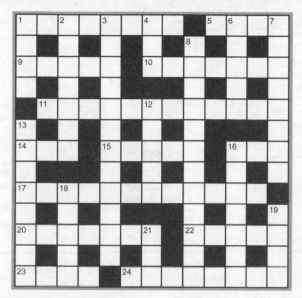

Across

1 Enter unlawfully (8)
5 Drive away (4)
9 Cotton twill fabric (5)
10 Foretell (7)
11 Build up again from parts (12)
14 E.g. pecan or cashew (3)
15 Curt (5)
16 One more than one (3)
17 A body of people forming a nation, state or community (12)
20 Trying experiences (7)
22 Lazes; does nothing (5)
23 Sell (anag.) (4)
24 Plot outline for a play (8)

Down

1 Thoughtfulness (4)
2 Obvious (7)
3 Commensurate (12)
4 Conciliatory gift (3)
6 Verse form (5)
7 Exactly on time (informal) (2,3,3)
8 Careful consideration (12)
12 Sharp-pointed metal pin (5)
13 Short account of an incident (8)
16 Nominal (7)
18 Scale representation (5)
19 Capital of Norway (4)
21 Intentionally so written (3)

CROSSWORD 55

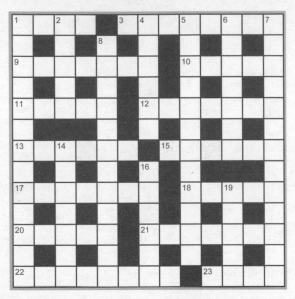

Across

1 Dull (4)
3 French bread stick (8)
9 Nerve impulses (7)
10 Meads (anag.) (5)
11 Chambers (5)
12 Rod used in weightlifting (7)
13 Entirely lacking (6)
15 Morsels of food (6)
17 People who rent property (7)
18 A point in question (5)
20 Promotional wording (5)
21 Pasta pockets (7)
22 Component parts (8)
23 Mob (4)

Down

1 Disreputable (13)
2 Friend (Spanish) (5)
4 With hands on the hips (6)
5 Perform below expectation (12)
6 Painting medium (7)
7 Style of popular music (4,9)
8 Uncertain (12)
14 Risky enterprise (7)
16 Sprightliness (6)
19 Minute pore (5)

CROSSWORD 56

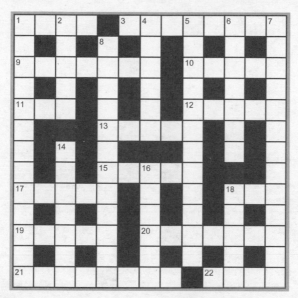

Across

1 Not at home (4)
3 Bitterness (8)
9 Educational establishment (7)
10 A satellite of Uranus (5)
11 Cry of a cat (3)
12 Balance (5)
13 Repeat the words of another (5)
15 Tree of the birch family (5)
17 Interior (5)
18 Give a nickname to (3)
19 Escape from (5)
20 Unit of sound intensity (7)
21 Wearisome (8)
22 Sea eagle (4)

Down

1 Supporting musical part (13)
2 Softly radiant (5)
4 Exaggerate (6)
5 Re-emergence (12)
6 Limiest (anag.) (7)
7 25th anniversary celebration (6,7)
8 Main premises of a company (12)
14 Vanquish (7)
16 Crown (6)
18 Suspend; prevent (5)

CROSSWORD 57

Across
1 Nourishment (4)
3 Exclamation of joy (8)
9 Learn new skills (7)
10 Grasp tightly (5)
11 Consumed (5)
12 Musical wind instrument (7)
13 Very dirty (6)
15 Part of a flower (6)
17 Brazilian dance (7)
18 Tortilla topped with cheese (5)
20 Precise (5)
21 Let out (7)
22 Bulbous plant (8)
23 Bone of the forearm (4)

Down
1 Absent-mindedness (13)
2 Group of eight (5)
4 Capital of England (6)
5 Bewitchingly (12)
6 Radioactive element (7)
7 The first and last (5,3,5)
8 Lacking courage (5-7)
14 Back pain (7)
16 Coiffure (6)
19 Move slowly (5)

CROSSWORD 58

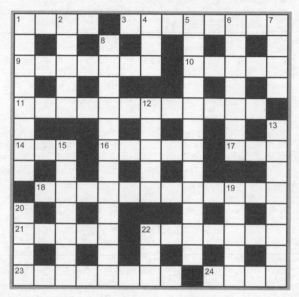

Across

1 Cipher (4)
3 Coldly detached (8)
9 Thinning out a tree by removing branches (7)
10 Variety or kind (5)
11 Prediction or expectation (12)
14 Male child (3)
16 Kick out (5)
17 19th Greek letter (3)
18 Able to use both hands well (12)
21 Circle a planet (5)
22 Surrendered (7)
23 Egg-laying mammal (8)
24 Push; poke (4)

Down

1 Cave in (8)
2 Storage place (5)
4 Fall behind (3)
5 Garments worn in bed (12)
6 Twist out of shape (7)
7 Reel (anag.) (4)
8 Science of biological processes (12)
12 Immature insects (5)
13 Became less intense (8)
15 African country with capital Windhoek (7)
19 More mature (5)
20 Splendid display (4)
22 Thee (3)

CROSSWORD 59

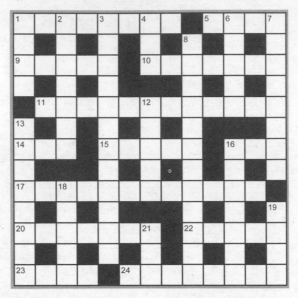

Across

1 Control (8)
5 Protective crust over a wound (4)
9 The furnishings in a room (5)
10 Keepsake; reminder (7)
11 Notwithstanding (12)
14 Frozen water (3)
15 Abominable snowmen (5)
16 Vitality (3)
17 Incomprehensibly (12)
20 Best (7)
22 Fishing net (5)
23 Forefather (4)
24 Uses a piece of machinery (8)

Down

1 Part of a pedestal (4)
2 Broad knife (7)
3 Short poem for children (7,5)
4 Unit of resistance (3)
6 Small boat (5)
7 Comes into flower (8)
8 Imitator (12)
12 Teacher (5)
13 Guests; callers (8)
16 Brave (7)
18 Supply with food (5)
19 Woes; problems (4)
21 Amp (anag.) (3)

CROSSWORD 60

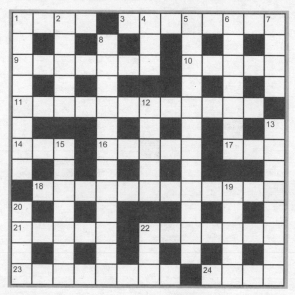

Across

1 Identical; unchanged (4)
3 Blushing with embarrassment (3-5)
9 Vast (7)
10 Strangely (5)
11 Intensely painful (12)
14 Excessively (3)
16 Liberates (5)
17 Mixture of gases we breathe (3)
18 Insensitive to criticism (5-7)
21 Lentil or chickpea (5)
22 Rider (7)
23 Farm vehicles (8)
24 Rip up (4)

Down

1 Sharp heel (8)
2 Impersonator (5)
4 Organ of sight (3)
5 Principal face of a building (12)
6 Virtuoso solo passage (7)
7 24-hour periods (4)
8 Inadequate (12)
12 Creative thoughts (5)
13 Animal that hunts (8)
15 Character in Hamlet (7)
19 Foolishly credulous (5)
20 Small fight (4)
22 Four-wheeled road vehicle (3)

CROSSWORD 61

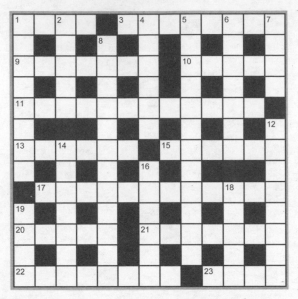

Across

1 Sweet dessert (4)
3 Curved sword (8)
9 Bring up (7)
10 Reversed (5)
11 Overstatement (12)
13 Flat; two-dimensional (6)
15 Throw in the towel (4,2)
17 Airing a TV program (12)
20 Seventh sign of the zodiac (5)
21 Mark written under the letter "C" (7)
22 12th month of the year (8)
23 Legendary story (4)

Down

1 Extreme reproach (8)
2 Destiny; fate (5)
4 Happy (6)
5 Hillside (12)
6 Larval frog (7)
7 Fishing sticks (4)
8 Electronic security device (7,5)
12 Engraved inscription (8)
14 Type of respiration (7)
16 Frozen water spear (6)
18 Embed; type of filling (5)
19 Trudge (4)

CROSSWORD 62

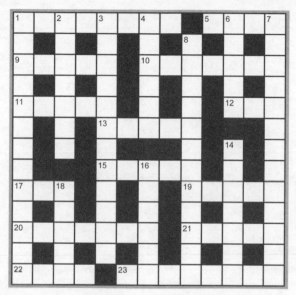

Across

1 Relating to the Middle Ages (8)
5 Cleanse (4)
9 Restraint for an animal (5)
10 Coincide partially (7)
11 Waggish (5)
12 State of armed conflict (3)
13 Many times (5)
15 Select; choose (5)
17 Not well (3)
19 Refute by evidence (5)
20 Quivering singing effect (7)
21 Staple (5)
22 Corrode (4)
23 Base of a statue (8)

Down

1 Manage badly (13)
2 Christian ministers (7)
3 Sensory system used by dolphins (12)
4 Apply ointment for religious reasons (6)
6 Permit (5)
7 Excessively negative about (13)
8 Clearly evident (12)
14 Look after an infant (7)
16 Serving no functional purpose (6)
18 Looks slyly (5)

CROSSWORD 63

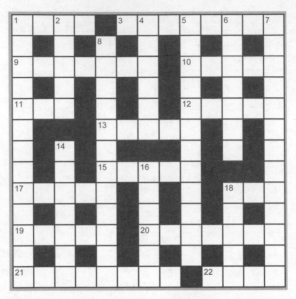

Across

1 Cried (4)
3 Device to keep rain out (8)
9 Refills (7)
10 Strength (5)
11 For each (3)
12 Path or road (5)
13 Loft (5)
15 Dividing boundaries (5)
17 Display freely (5)
18 Sum charged (3)
19 Show indifference with the shoulders (5)
20 Break an agreement (7)
21 Flower-shaped competition awards (8)
22 Creative disciplines (4)

Down

1 Computer program for writing documents (4,9)
2 Lighter (5)
4 Outsider (6)
5 Consequence of an event (12)
6 Civil action brought to court (7)
7 Pleasantness (13)
8 Boxing class (12)
14 Multiplies a number by itself (7)
16 French museum (6)
18 Talent; ability (5)

CROSSWORD 64

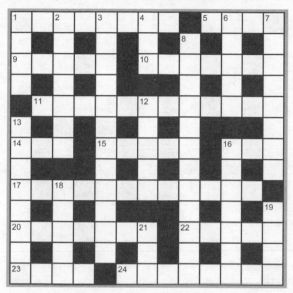

Across

1 Clearly defined area (8)
5 Main island of Indonesia (4)
9 Earlier (5)
10 Forbidden by law (7)
11 Re-evaluation (12)
14 Nevertheless (3)
15 Personnel at work (5)
16 Type of statistical chart (3)
17 Practice of designing buildings (12)
20 Effluence (7)
22 Tines (anag.) (5)
23 Repetition of a sound (4)
24 Country in Asia (8)

Down

1 Catholic leader (4)
2 Urgent (7)
3 Overwhelmingly compelling (12)
4 22nd Greek letter (3)
6 Standpoint (5)
7 Sparkling (8)
8 Tight (of clothing) (5-7)
12 Fill with high spirits (5)
13 Large Eurasian maple (8)
16 Act of reading carefully (7)
18 Receive a ball in one's hands (5)
19 Volcano in Sicily (4)
21 Court (3)

CROSSWORD 65

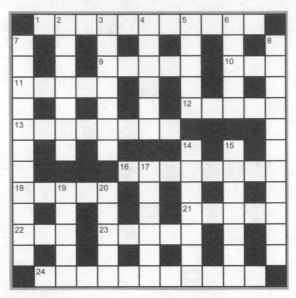

Across

- 1 Incorporating sound and images (11)
- 9 Foreign language (informal) (5)
- 10 Domesticated pig (3)
- 11 Strong lightweight wood (5)
- 12 Of the nose (5)
- 13 Reference point; norm (8)
- 16 An opening (8)
- 18 Sum; add up (5)
- 21 Striped animal (5)
- 22 Item for catching fish (3)
- 23 Precious gem (5)
- 24 Not having a written constitution (11)

Down

- 2 Uncertain (7)
- 3 E.g. Borneo and Java (7)
- 4 Thin decorative coating (6)
- 5 Exhibited (5)
- 6 Pains (5)
- 7 Act of looking after children (11)
- 8 Form into a cluster (11)
- 14 Make mentally fatigued (7)
- 15 Tribune (anag.) (7)
- 17 Pungent condiment (6)
- 19 Largest moon of Saturn (5)
- 20 Gate fastener (5)

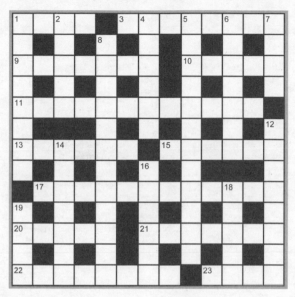

Across

1 Expose to danger (4)
3 Dismiss as unimportant (5,3)
9 Leopard (7)
10 Later (5)
11 Withdraw from service (12)
13 Oppressively hot (6)
15 Fortitude (6)
17 Evening dress for men (6,6)
20 The beginning of an era (5)
21 Very large; clumsy (7)
22 Wide-ranging (8)
23 Feeling of strong eagerness (4)

Down

1 Swiftness (8)
2 Pertaining to sound (5)
4 Very brave and courageous (6)
5 Not capable of reply (12)
6 Distant settlement (7)
7 Shallow river crossing (4)
8 Type of contest (12)
12 Polygon with five sides (8)
14 Horizontal plant stem (7)
16 Young child who is poorly dressed (6)
18 Tiny crustaceans (5)
19 Writing implements (4)

CROSSWORD 67

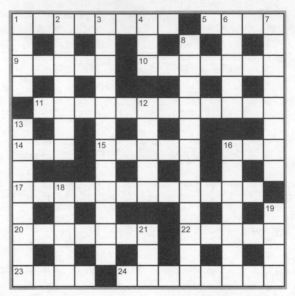

Across

1 Lacking confidence (8)
5 Finished; complete (4)
9 Monotonous hum (5)
10 Feared greatly (7)
11 Loving (12)
14 Put down (3)
15 Small branch (5)
16 Enemy (3)
17 Connection or association (12)
20 Unit of electric charge (7)
22 Frighten; warning sound (5)
23 Right to hold property (4)
24 Opposite of northern (8)

Down

1 After the beginning of (4)
2 Untidy (7)
3 Reparation (12)
4 Relieve or free from (3)
6 Russian spirit (5)
7 Blushed (8)
8 Medicine taken when blocked-up (12)
12 Trunk of the body (5)
13 Relating to office work (8)
16 Warship (7)
18 Ousel (anag.) (5)
19 So be it (4)
21 Cry of disapproval (3)

CROSSWORD 68

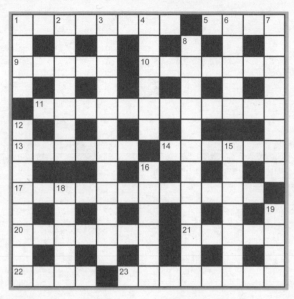

Across

1 Arriving (8)
5 Bend over upon itself (4)
9 Cloth woven from flax (5)
10 Coolness (7)
11 Major type of food nutrient (12)
13 Motor vehicle storage building (6)
14 Avoids (6)
17 Dictatorial (12)
20 Capital of Ontario (7)
21 Model; perfect (5)
22 Extinct bird (4)
23 Naive or sentimental (4-4)

Down

1 Lazy (4)
2 Mythical being (7)
3 Startling (4-8)
4 Equine sounds (6)
6 Last Greek letter (5)
7 Distribute (8)
8 Variety of wildlife in an area (12)
12 Excited or annoyed (8)
15 Group of parishes (7)
16 Flash intermittently (6)
18 Weary (5)
19 Lids (anag.) (4)

CROSSWORD 69

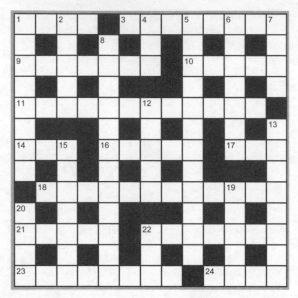

Across

1 Mountain top (4)
3 People with auburn hair (8)
9 Matured (7)
10 Musical note (5)
11 Smooth and easy progress (5,7)
14 Cause friction (3)
16 Tests (5)
17 Fasten with stitches (3)
18 Impudence (12)
21 Timber beam (5)
22 Not friendly (7)
23 Lack of flexibility (8)
24 Poses a question (4)

Down

1 Sweat (8)
2 First Greek letter (5)
4 Cease (3)
5 Vagrancy (12)
6 Canvas shelters (7)
7 Unspecified in number (4)
8 Indifferent to (12)
12 Expect (5)
13 Small loudspeakers (8)
15 Knocking into (7)
19 Metal spikes (5)
20 Partly open (4)
22 Smack (3)

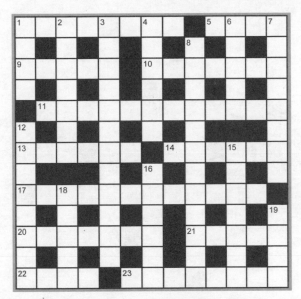

Across

1 Married men (8)
5 Stylish and fashionable (4)
9 Studies and comprehends text (5)
10 Improve (7)
11 Large grocery stores (12)
13 Sloping (of a typeface) (6)
14 Thoroughfare (6)
17 Developmental (12)
20 Devise beforehand (7)
21 Up to the time when (5)
22 Home for a bird (4)
23 Spice (8)

Down

1 Solid (4)
2 Kitchen implement (7)
3 In a sparing manner (12)
4 You may have these while asleep (6)
6 Therefore (5)
7 Wood preserver (8)
8 Having an acrid wit (5-7)
12 Longevity of an individual (8)
15 Mistake in printing or writing (7)
16 Yellowish-brown pigment (6)
18 Follows orders (5)
19 Chemical salt used in dyeing (4)

CROSSWORD 71

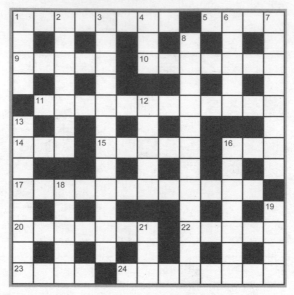

Across

1 Traitor (8)
5 Suggestion (4)
9 Private room on a ship (5)
10 Type of dance (3-4)
11 Insincere (12)
14 Carry a heavy object (3)
15 Deprive of weapons (5)
16 Snip (3)
17 Excessively forward (12)
20 Envelops (7)
22 Coldly (5)
23 Spun thread used for knitting (4)
24 Three-hulled sailing boat (8)

Down

1 Short nail (4)
2 Stealing (7)
3 Endlessly (12)
4 Statute (3)
6 Mark of repetition (5)
7 Of striking appropriateness (8)
8 Sleepwalking (12)
12 Seize firmly (5)
13 Unreliable; shifty (8)
16 Messenger (7)
18 Keen (5)
19 Church song (4)
21 A knight (3)

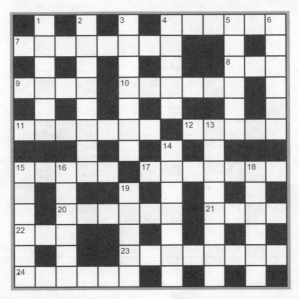

Across

4 Child (6)
7 Joke-telling entertainer (8)
8 Female pronoun (3)
9 Cab (4)
10 Arise from (6)
11 Shooting stars (7)
12 Neck warmer (5)
15 Single-edged hunting knife (5)
17 Perform in an exaggerated manner (7)
20 Expose as being false (6)
21 By word of mouth (4)
22 Affirmative vote (3)
23 Liking for something (8)
24 Stomach crunches (3-3)

Down

1 Quantity of medicine to take (6)
2 Disease caused by a lack of thiamine (8)
3 Burnt fragments of wood (7)
4 Accustom (5)
5 Greek goddess of wisdom (6)
6 Duty or tax (6)
13 Animated drawings (8)
14 Conjuring up feelings (7)
15 Beards (anag.) (6)
16 Broadest (6)
18 Unrefined (6)
19 Polishes (5)

CROSSWORD 73

Across

1 Negotiator (8)
5 Primates (4)
9 Tropical fruit (5)
10 Works in an amateurish way (7)
11 Hostile aggressiveness (12)
14 Touch gently (3)
15 Short and sweet (5)
16 Mainly nocturnal mammal (3)
17 Remembrance (12)
20 Spacecraft that circles the planet (7)
22 Moisten meat (5)
23 Froth of soap and water (4)
24 Whole; complete (8)

Down

1 Wizard (4)
2 Form of speech specific to a region (7)
3 Quality of being at hand when necessary (12)
4 Not in (3)
6 Smooth; groom (5)
7 Believes tentatively (8)
8 Making no money (12)
12 Dirt (5)
13 Not genuine (8)
16 Program for viewing web pages (7)
18 Raised to the third power (5)
19 Head covering (4)
21 Sprinted (3)

CROSSWORD 74

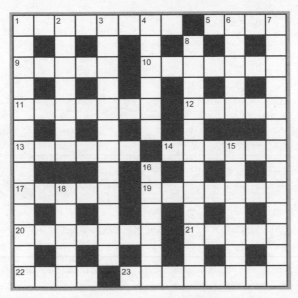

Across

1 Flight of steps (8)
5 Bitter-tasting substance (4)
9 Our planet (5)
10 Witty saying (7)
11 Dressed in a vestment (7)
12 Speck of food (5)
13 Push over (6)
14 Measure of heaviness (6)
17 Suggest (5)
19 State of the USA (7)
20 Having an obscure meaning (7)
21 One of the United Arab Emirates (5)
22 Puts down (4)
23 Short heavy club (8)

Down

1 Lacking originality (13)
2 Deliver by parachute (3-4)
3 Restore to good condition (12)
4 Edits (6)
6 The papal court (5)
7 Presentation on how to use something (13)
8 Very determined (6-6)
15 Farewell remark (7)
16 Scoundrel (6)
18 Craftily (5)

CROSSWORD 75

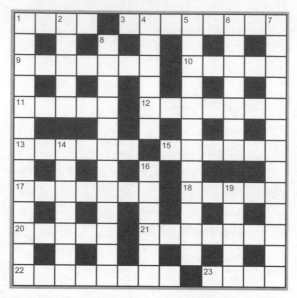

Across

1 Falls back (4)
3 Assimilate again (8)
9 Clear mess away (5,2)
10 Capital of Egypt (5)
11 Wedding official (5)
12 Intimidate (7)
13 Extraterrestrials (6)
15 Terminate (6)
17 Distinguished (7)
18 Assumed proposition (5)
20 Strike out; omit (5)
21 Fail to care for (7)
22 Red fruits eaten as vegetables (8)
23 Sued (anag.) (4)

Down

1 Expression of approval (13)
2 Large tree (5)
4 Give a job to (6)
5 Study of microorganisms (12)
6 Paper folding (7)
7 Overwhelmed with sorrow (6-7)
8 Action of breaking a law (12)
14 Metal similar to platinum (7)
16 Body position (6)
19 Encounters (5)

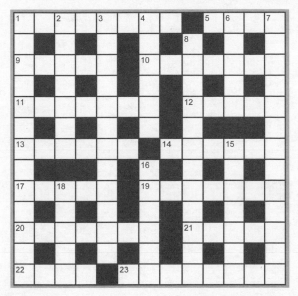

Across

1 Coal mine (8)
5 Silvery-white metallic element (4)
9 Automaton (5)
10 Highest singing voice (7)
11 Becomes established in a new place (7)
12 Type of verse (5)
13 Scandinavian (6)
14 Throwing at a target (6)
17 Animal used for riding (5)
19 Venetian boat (7)
20 Country in northwestern Africa (7)
21 Nationality of Oscar Wilde (5)
22 Intellectual faculty (4)
23 Person aged 13 - 19 (8)

Down

1 Plant with bright flowers (13)
2 Large crustacean (7)
3 Ability to acquire and apply knowledge (12)
4 Oppose (6)
6 Where one finds Rome (5)
7 Musical dance coordinator (13)
8 Foreboding (12)
15 Smoothing clothes (7)
16 Pay no attention to (6)
18 Broadcast again (5)

CROSSWORD 77

Across

1 Opposite of west (4)
3 African country (8)
9 Less dirty (7)
10 Name of a book (5)
11 Surpassing in influence (12)
13 Cease (6)
15 State of the USA (6)
17 Excessively loud (12)
20 Momentary oversight (5)
21 Young chicken (7)
22 Least lengthy (8)
23 Jar lids (4)

Down

1 Wild prank (8)
2 Type of leather (5)
4 Vehement speech (6)
5 Act of seizing something en route (12)
6 Garden flower (7)
7 Affirm with confidence (4)
8 Not staying the same throughout (12)
12 Dawdlers (8)
14 Hair-cleansing product (7)
16 Spherical objects (6)
18 Ice home (5)
19 Deciduous trees (4)

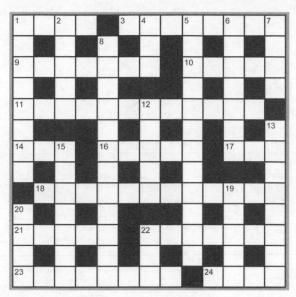

Across

1 Ridge of rock (4)
3 E.g. a spider or scorpion (8)
9 Small crown (7)
10 Assesses performance (5)
11 Branch of astronomy (12)
14 Space or interval (3)
16 Snake toxin (5)
17 One more than five (3)
18 Most perfect example of a quality (12)
21 ___ Agassi: former tennis star (5)
22 Gadgets (7)
23 Patrimony (8)
24 Wagers (4)

Down

1 Reload (8)
2 White waterbird (5)
4 Mud channel (3)
5 24th December (9,3)
6 Observes (7)
7 Office table (4)
8 Awkward; untimely (12)
12 Door hanger (5)
13 Overabundances (8)
15 Pillage (7)
19 Mother-of-pearl (5)
20 Whip (4)
22 Canine (3)

CROSSWORD 79

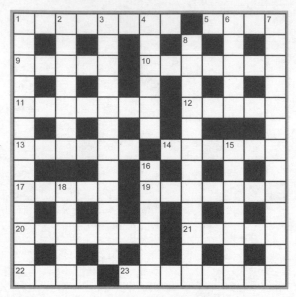

Across

1 Exceptional (8)
5 Foolish (4)
9 Palpitate (5)
10 Carry out an action (7)
11 A rich mine; big prize (7)
12 Stanza or verse (5)
13 Contributes information (6)
14 Figure of speech (6)
17 Doglike mammal (5)
19 Quarrel or haggle (7)
20 Beg (7)
21 Small island (5)
22 Period of imprisonment (4)
23 About-face (8)

Down

1 Institution (13)
2 Root vegetable (7)
3 Skilled joiner (12)
4 Be attractive (6)
6 Hawaiian greeting (5)
7 Unpredictable (13)
8 Question in great detail (5-7)
15 Laughs (7)
16 Bandage (6)
18 Come in (5)

CROSSWORD 80

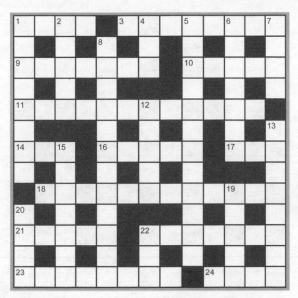

Across

- **1** Floor coverings (4)
- **3** Cuts into bits (8)
- **9** Tidy (5,2)
- **10** Denim (anag.) (5)
- **11** Omit too much detail (12)
- **14** The gist of the matter (3)
- **16** Programmer (5)
- **17** Regret with sadness (3)
- **18** Made (12)
- **21** Not heavy (5)
- **22** Visibly anxious (7)
- **23** Fretting (8)
- **24** Percussion instrument (4)

Down

- **1** Furry nocturnal mammals (8)
- **2** Diving waterbird (5)
- **4** Sprite (3)
- **5** Areas of commonality (12)
- **6** Needle-leaved tree (7)
- **7** Team (4)
- **8** Long athletics race (5-7)
- **12** E.g. newspapers and TV (5)
- **13** Clock timing device (8)
- **15** Very boastful person (7)
- **19** Touch on; mention (5)
- **20** Sudden misfortune (4)
- **22** Fish appendage (3)

CROSSWORD 81

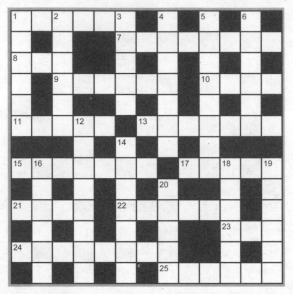

Across

1 Body of running water (6)
7 Incessant (8)
8 Was in first place (3)
9 Hesitate (6)
10 Cooking appliance (4)
11 Verbose (5)
13 Junction between nerve cells (7)
15 Courage (7)
17 Under (5)
21 Morally wicked (4)
22 Material; textile (6)
23 Unit of current (3)
24 Cold Spanish tomato soup (8)
25 Explanation (6)

Down

1 Jaundiced (6)
2 Steering mechanism of a boat (6)
3 Pulpy (5)
4 Acts in a disloyal manner (7)
5 Publicly recommend (8)
6 Smiles contemptuously (6)
12 Makes more elaborate (8)
14 Introduction to a book (7)
16 Expose (6)
18 Residents of an area (6)
19 Fighting instrument (6)
20 Loathe (5)

CROSSWORD 82

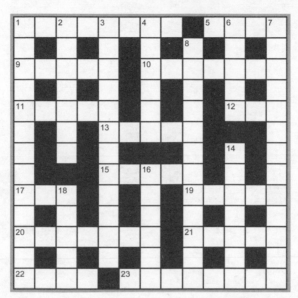

Across

1 Teachers (anag.) (8)
5 Metallic element (4)
9 Circumference (5)
10 Snake (7)
11 Make amends (5)
12 Sense of self-esteem (3)
13 One who avoids animal products (5)
15 Type of coffee drink (5)
17 Deep anger (3)
19 Japanese dish (5)
20 Natural environment (7)
21 Gold block (5)
22 Coniferous trees of the genus Taxus (4)
23 Relating to critical explanation (8)

Down

1 Autocratic (4-3-6)
2 Orange vegetables (7)
3 Accomplishments (12)
4 Relaxing (6)
6 Pass a rope through (5)
7 Patriotic (13)
8 Forcible indoctrination (12)
14 Clear perception (7)
16 Outer layer of the cerebrum (6)
18 Arm joint (5)

CROSSWORD 83

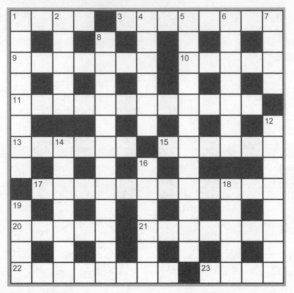

Across

- **1** Egg-shaped (4)
- **3** Beautiful mausoleum at Agra (3,5)
- **9** Diplomatic building (7)
- **10** Company emblems (5)
- **11** Caused by disease (12)
- **13** Ghost (6)
- **15** One under par in golf (6)
- **17** Based on legend (12)
- **20** Research deeply (5)
- **21** Flee (7)
- **22** And so on (2,6)
- **23** Parched (4)

Down

- **1** Bridge above another road (8)
- **2** Scope or extent (5)
- **4** In a careless manner (6)
- **5** Knowing more than one language (12)
- **6** Gaunt (7)
- **7** One of the seven deadly sins (4)
- **8** Amazement (12)
- **12** Stated emphatically (8)
- **14** Delightful (7)
- **16** Nearer (6)
- **18** Escapade (5)
- **19** Corner (4)

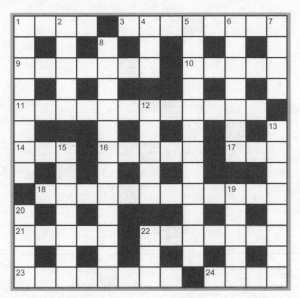

Across

1 Sheet of paper in a book (4)
3 Complete loss of electrical power (8)
9 In an unspecified manner (7)
10 Irritable (5)
11 Middleman (12)
14 Research place (abbrev.) (3)
16 Excessively mean (5)
17 How (anag.) (3)
18 Beneficial (12)
21 With a forward motion (5)
22 Item of clerical clothing (7)
23 Atmospheric moisture (8)
24 Biblical garden (4)

Down

1 Capable of happening (8)
2 The entire scale (5)
4 Opposite of high (3)
5 Heart specialist (12)
6 Get too big for something (7)
7 Playthings (4)
8 Cheated someone financially (5-7)
12 Break out with force (5)
13 Abandoned (8)
15 Where you sleep (7)
19 Egg-shaped solid (5)
20 Large washing bowl (4)
22 Bed for a baby (3)

CROSSWORD 85

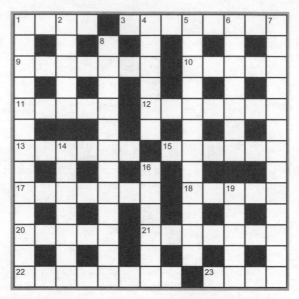

Across

1 Curved shapes (4)
3 Explosively unstable (8)
9 Non-specific (7)
10 Become ready to eat (of fruit) (5)
11 Spiritual nourishment (5)
12 Stipulation (7)
13 Subtle detail (6)
15 Central parts of cells (6)
17 Device that measures electric current (7)
18 Shadow (5)
20 Adult insect stage (5)
21 Tidal wave (7)
22 Admired and respected (8)
23 Adolescent (abbrev.) (4)

Down

1 Given to debate (13)
2 Body of rules (5)
4 Hold a position or job (6)
5 Type of cloud (12)
6 Pertaining to marriage (7)
7 Act of combining into a solid mass (13)
8 Swimming technique (12)
14 Reduce in size (7)
16 Contort (6)
19 Edge of a knife (5)

CROSSWORD 86

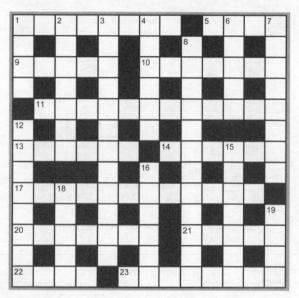

Across

1 Trachea (8)
5 Low dull sound (4)
9 Less common (5)
10 Drives aground (a boat) (7)
11 Disheartening (12)
13 Recover (6)
14 Three times (6)
17 Deceiver (6-6)
20 Distinct sentence parts (7)
21 State of the USA (5)
22 Case of film (4)
23 Female offspring (8)

Down

1 Watchful (4)
2 Caring for (7)
3 Provincialism (12)
4 Show-off (6)
6 Capital of Vietnam (5)
7 Made with purpose; planned (8)
8 Awe-inspiring (12)
12 Manufacturer (8)
15 Imprecise (7)
16 Ukrainian port (6)
18 Customary practice (5)
19 Not sweet (4)

CROSSWORD 87

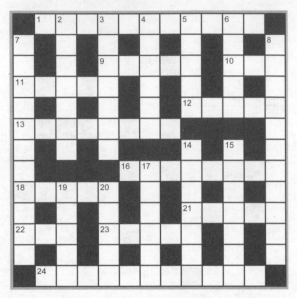

Across

- **1** Philosophical doctrine (11)
- **9** The beginning of something (5)
- **10** Cooling tool (3)
- **11** Angered; irritated (5)
- **12** Mournful song (5)
- **13** Madness (8)
- **16** Musical pieces for solo instruments (8)
- **18** Felts (anag.) (5)
- **21** Machine for shaping wood or metal (5)
- **22** Large dark antelope (3)
- **23** Small white garden flower (5)
- **24** Pairs of round brackets (11)

Down

- **2** Interminable (7)
- **3** Wearing away (7)
- **4** Thing that brings good luck (6)
- **5** Observed (5)
- **6** More secure (5)
- **7** Phraseology (11)
- **8** Clever (11)
- **14** Assistant; follower (7)
- **15** Chatter on and on (7)
- **17** Musician playing a double-reed instrument (6)
- **19** Animal life of a region (5)
- **20** Move sideways (5)

CROSSWORD 88

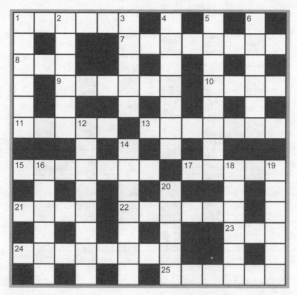

Across

1 Right to enter (6)
7 Fighters (8)
8 Long period of time (3)
9 Small cake (6)
10 Makes brown (4)
11 Vault under a church (5)
13 Given; bequeathed (7)
15 Inert gaseous element (7)
17 Lifting device (5)
21 Piece of evidence (4)
22 Summon; telephone (4,2)
23 Fruit of a rose (3)
24 Catch a conversation between others (8)
25 Reply (6)

Down

1 Pertaining to vinegar (6)
2 Damp and sticky to touch (6)
3 Fast (5)
4 Cutting back a tree (7)
5 Brilliant performers (8)
6 Copper and tin alloy (6)
12 Act of operating marionettes (8)
14 One who hunts illegally (7)
16 Experience again (6)
18 Son of one's brother or sister (6)
19 Aide (6)
20 Plants of a region (5)

CROSSWORD 89

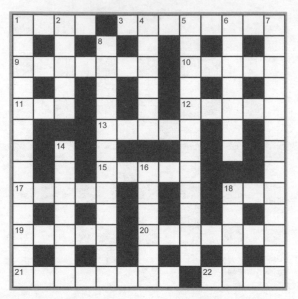

Across

1 Imperial unit (4)
3 Industrious (8)
9 Competitors in a sprint (7)
10 At that place; not here (5)
11 Express in words (3)
12 Armature of a generator (5)
13 Stares with the mouth wide open (5)
15 Loose, sleeveless garment (5)
17 Rigid (5)
18 Twitch (3)
19 Become very hot (5)
20 Breathing aid in water (7)
21 Author (8)
22 Hunted animal (4)

Down

1 Untrustworthy (13)
2 Shrewd (5)
4 Arch of the foot (6)
5 Junction (12)
6 Brought to bear (7)
7 Conceptually (13)
8 Charmingly (12)
14 Destructive (7)
16 Hospital carers (6)
18 Buyer (5)

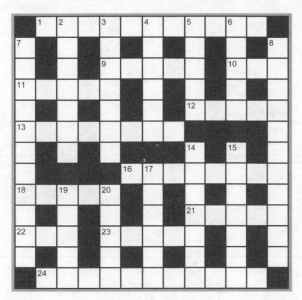

Across

1 Happening in stages (11)
9 Relating to sound (5)
10 Jewel (3)
11 Certain to end in failure (2-3)
12 Make less miserable (5)
13 Early period of human culture (5,3)
16 Makers (8)
18 Delete (5)
21 Juicy fruit (5)
22 Metal container (3)
23 Unwarranted (5)
24 Devices popular before computers existed (11)

Down

2 Huge coniferous tree (7)
3 Admittedly (7)
4 Finish (6)
5 Indifferent to emotions (5)
6 Not clearly stated (5)
7 Infinite knowledge (11)
8 Impersonations (11)
14 Hottest (7)
15 Fill with water and sink (of a ship) (7)
17 University lecturer (6)
19 Harass; frustrate (5)
20 Draw or bring out (5)

CROSSWORD 91

Across

1 Stayed in place (8)
5 Moist (4)
8 Parts of eggs (5)
9 Walked heavily and firmly (7)
10 Requiring (7)
12 Knife attached to a rifle (7)
14 Soon (7)
16 Juicy soft fruit (7)
18 Examine (7)
19 Lowest point (5)
20 Unit of heredity (4)
21 Keep at a distance (8)

Down

1 Light beams from the sun (4)
2 Tune (6)
3 Someone who cannot sleep (9)
4 Still existing (6)
6 Domestic assistant (2,4)
7 Method and practice of teaching (8)
11 Something that is revealing (3-6)
12 Making inoperative (8)
13 Jail (6)
14 Expresses one's opinion (6)
15 Connective tissue (6)
17 At liberty (4)

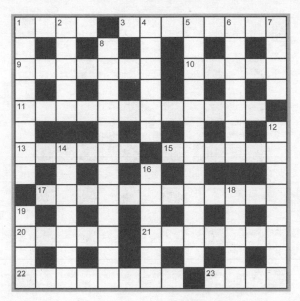

Across

1 Buckles (4)
3 Brawny (8)
9 Wishes for (7)
10 Bond or connection (5)
11 Lack of practical knowledge (12)
13 Raise in relief (6)
15 Street (6)
17 Jail term without end (4,8)
20 Surpass (5)
21 Restoration to life (7)
22 Household implements (8)
23 Delighted (4)

Down

1 Sheets and pillowcases (8)
2 Use inefficiently (5)
4 Uncertain (6)
5 Resistant to change (12)
6 Vocabulary of a person (7)
7 Optimistic (4)
8 Absurd (12)
12 Revoked a law (8)
14 Stiff coarse hair (7)
16 Pertaining to a nerve (6)
18 A central point (5)
19 Product made from soya beans (4)

CROSSWORD 93

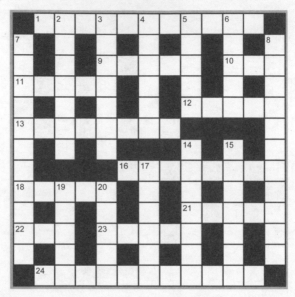

Across

1 Masterpiece (4,2,5)
9 Locates or places (5)
10 Expected at a certain time (3)
11 Hard outgrowths on animals (5)
12 Tennis stroke (5)
13 Capable of being used (8)
16 Renounce or reject (8)
18 Stitched (5)
21 Circular in shape (5)
22 Wonder (3)
23 Corpulent (5)
24 Relating to fireworks (11)

Down

2 Supervise (7)
3 E.g. from Moscow (7)
4 Impose or require (6)
5 Fertile area in a desert (5)
6 Alcoholic drink made from apples (5)
7 Substance that arouses desire (11)
8 Calm and sensible (5-6)
14 Renew (7)
15 Bathing tub with bubbles (7)
17 Current of air (6)
19 Tearful (5)
20 Italian cathedral (5)

CROSSWORD 94

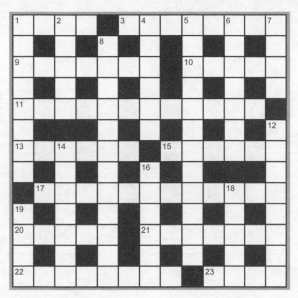

Across

1 Shallow food container (4)
3 Corrosive precipitation (4,4)
9 Looks over in detail (7)
10 Doctor (5)
11 Awkward (12)
13 Unkempt (of hair) (6)
15 In a lively manner (6)
17 Carport choir (anag.) (12)
20 Rupture (5)
21 Oval shape (7)
22 Preserve or hold sacred (8)
23 Chances of winning (4)

Down

1 Spread out (8)
2 Small woody plant (5)
4 Offhand (6)
5 Nationally (12)
6 Additions to a document (7)
7 Slight cut (4)
8 Cooling device (12)
12 Intrepid; courageous (8)
14 Sticks to (7)
16 Abdominal organ (6)
18 Used a computer keyboard (5)
19 Double-reed instrument (4)

CROSSWORD 95

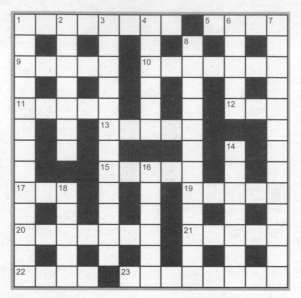

Across

1 Intended to teach (8)
5 Flightless bird (4)
9 Practice of lending money at high interest rates (5)
10 Mundane (7)
11 Threshold (5)
12 Rocky peak (3)
13 Relating to vision (5)
15 Judged; ranked (5)
17 Climbing plant (3)
19 Turn inside out (5)
20 Windpipe (7)
21 Part of the hand (5)
22 Facts and statistics collectively (4)
23 Come together (8)

Down

1 Having unusually flexible joints (6-7)
2 Percussion musician (7)
3 Science of deciphering codes (12)
4 Bring into the country (6)
6 Paint (anag.) (5)
7 Forever honest (13)
8 Occurring at the same time (12)
14 Streets (7)
16 Red salad fruit (6)
18 Microscopic fungus (5)

CROSSWORD 96

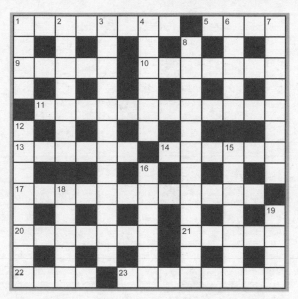

Across

1 Throaty (of a speech sound) (8)
5 Among (4)
9 Elevated step (5)
10 Books of maps (7)
11 Highly abstract (12)
13 State of the USA (6)
14 Glowing remains of a fire (6)
17 Bravely (12)
20 Decide firmly (7)
21 Hang in the air (5)
22 Oust (anag.) (4)
23 Forgave (8)

Down

1 Flow copiously (4)
2 Circus apparatus (7)
3 Not guided by good sense (12)
4 Absence of passion (6)
6 Agreeable sound or tune (5)
7 Make information known (8)
8 Reticent and secretive (12)
12 Musical composition (8)
15 Make more entertaining (7)
16 Taxonomic groupings (6)
18 Surprise result (5)
19 Network of lines (4)

CROSSWORD 97

Across

1 Bog (8)
5 Pal (4)
9 Tripod for an artist (5)
10 Grumbled (7)
11 Like a bull (7)
12 Go to see (5)
13 Expenditure (6)
14 Engineless aircraft (6)
17 Courage; boldness (5)
19 Plant with starchy tuberous roots (7)
20 A precise point in time (7)
21 Follow on (5)
22 Otherwise (4)
23 Keep under control (8)

Down

1 Survey (13)
2 Attack (7)
3 Agreed upon by several parties (12)
4 Having a rough surface (of terrain) (6)
6 Assembly rooms (5)
7 Large sea (13)
8 Recovering from illness (of a person) (12)
15 Salt lake in the Jordan valley (4,3)
16 Hay-cutting tool (6)
18 Takes a break (5)

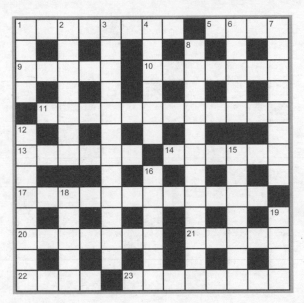

Across

1 Large cask (8)
5 Continent (4)
9 Excuse or pretext (5)
10 Horizontal angle of a compass bearing (7)
11 Not allowable (12)
13 Person staying in another's home (6)
14 Multiply by three (6)
17 Tamed (12)
20 Aims or purposes (7)
21 Clumsy (5)
22 Breathe convulsively (4)
23 Classic US comedy TV series (8)

Down

1 Pile (4)
2 Smiled broadly (7)
3 Radishes grin (anag.) (12)
4 Leguminous tree (6)
6 Small firework (5)
7 Accomplished (8)
8 Long essay (12)
12 Trudging (8)
15 Go before (7)
16 Fine cloth (6)
18 Legendary stories (5)
19 Metal fastener (4)

CROSSWORD 99

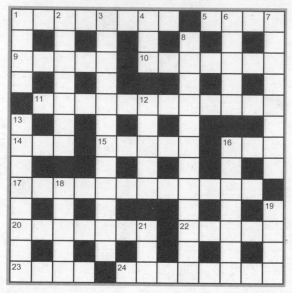

Across

- **1** Compassion (8)
- **5** Freezes over (4)
- **9** Precious stone (5)
- **10** Eighth sign of the zodiac (7)
- **11** Unemotional and practical (6-2-4)
- **14** Auction offer (3)
- **15** Measuring stick (5)
- **16** Pop music performance (3)
- **17** Not discernible (12)
- **20** Fire-breathing creatures (7)
- **22** Relation by marriage (2-3)
- **23** Ivy League university (4)
- **24** Woody (8)

Down

- **1** Cries (4)
- **2** Mythical female sea creature (7)
- **3** Repetition of the same sound (12)
- **4** Belonging to him (3)
- **6** Dried kernel of the coconut (5)
- **7** Paucity (8)
- **8** Shape of something (12)
- **12** Ancient object (5)
- **13** Ridiculously (8)
- **16** US space probe to Jupiter (7)
- **18** Speak in a slow manner (5)
- **19** Woes (anag.) (4)
- **21** Snow runner (3)

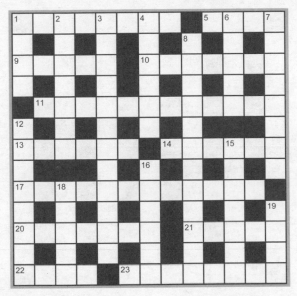

Across

1 Connected (8)
5 Business (4)
9 Red-chested bird (5)
10 Newspaper audience (7)
11 Creator of film scripts (12)
13 Sags (6)
14 Flies down rapidly (6)
17 Penny-pinching (12)
20 Pancreatic hormone (7)
21 Condescend (5)
22 Obtains (4)
23 Feud (8)

Down

1 Distinctive atmosphere created by a person (4)
2 Cigarette constituent (7)
3 Despicable (12)
4 Straying from the right course (6)
6 Inactive (5)
7 Be suspicious of (8)
8 Lacking tolerance or flexibility (6-6)
12 Changing (8)
15 Type of optician (7)
16 Living room (6)
18 Restore factory settings (5)
19 ___ Kournikova: former tennis star (4)

CROSSWORD 101

Across

1 Fraudulently (11)
9 Find an answer to (5)
10 Pair of people (3)
11 Stringed instruments (5)
12 Angry dispute (3-2)
13 Adversary (8)
16 Certificates of education (8)
18 Conceals (5)
21 Work at a loom (5)
22 Gang (3)
23 Confound (5)
24 Condition in an agreement (11)

Down

2 Form of an element (7)
3 Sibilant (7)
4 Wrestling hold (6)
5 Absolute (5)
6 Burdened (5)
7 General guideline (4,2,5)
8 Expert critic (11)
14 Tardiest (7)
15 Ban on publication (7)
17 Country in the Middle East (6)
19 A payment made (5)
20 Skin on top of the head (5)

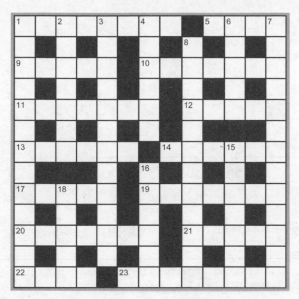

Across

1 Moving slowly (8)
5 Adhesive (4)
9 Shallow recess (5)
10 Move something; agitate (7)
11 Apprentice (7)
12 Regal (5)
13 Masticated (6)
14 Opposite of an acid (6)
17 Leers (5)
19 Mischievous (7)
20 Spanish beverage (7)
21 Felony (5)
22 Three-feet length (4)
23 Small window (8)

Down

1 Prominently (13)
2 Shut in (7)
3 Forerunners (12)
4 Indicated assent (6)
6 Very bad (5)
7 Ornamentation (13)
8 Relating to horoscopes (12)
15 Enduring (7)
16 Printed mistakes (6)
18 Pertaining to the moon (5)

CROSSWORD 103

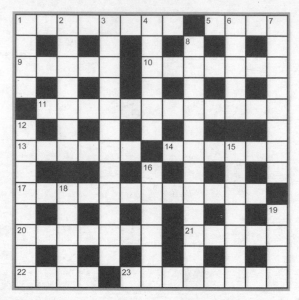

Across

1 Creating needless panic (8)
5 Give out (4)
9 Warms up (5)
10 Porch (7)
11 Erase trumpet (anag.) (12)
13 Implant deeply (6)
14 Hinder (6)
17 Obfuscation (12)
20 Savings for the future (4,3)
21 Enclosed (of animals) (5)
22 Utters (4)
23 Hairdressers (8)

Down

1 Having pains (4)
2 Non-professional (7)
3 Made in bulk (4-8)
4 Harsh (6)
6 Lesser (5)
7 Move to another place (8)
8 Relating to numeric calculations (12)
12 Women noted for great courage (8)
15 Banners or flags (7)
16 Educated (6)
18 Impudent; full of spirit (5)
19 Lyric poems (4)

CROSSWORD 104

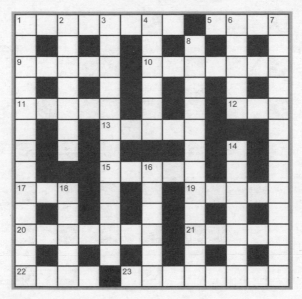

Across

1 Large metal pot (8)
5 Popular martial art (4)
9 Ponders (5)
10 Elusive (7)
11 Entertain (5)
12 Positive answer (3)
13 Nuisances (5)
15 Underground enlarged stem (5)
17 Fantastical creature (3)
19 Unit of weight (5)
20 Fifth Greek letter (7)
21 Vast multitude (5)
22 Loop of cloth worn around the waist (4)
23 Wristband (8)

Down

1 Militant aggressiveness (13)
2 Defective (7)
3 Discreditable (12)
4 Musical dramas (6)
6 Oneness (5)
7 Exaggeration (13)
8 Extremely harmful (12)
14 Solid inorganic substance (7)
16 Website advertisement (6)
18 Clenched hands (5)

CROSSWORD 105

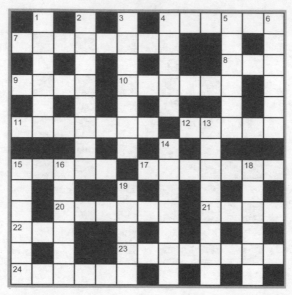

Across

4 Opposite of open (6)
7 Lazy (8)
8 Clumsy person (3)
9 Cool and collected (4)
10 Zone (6)
11 Characteristics (7)
12 Herb (5)
15 Venomous snake (5)
17 Write again (7)
20 Post (6)
21 Religious sisters (4)
22 Zero (3)
23 Deplorably (8)
24 Fashions (6)

Down

1 Makes a weak cry (of sheep) (6)
2 Mad rush (8)
3 Compensates for (7)
4 Become suddenly understandable (5)
5 Casual but stylish (of clothing) (6)
6 State the meaning of (6)
13 Lecture forcefully (8)
14 University qualifications (7)
15 Stadiums (6)
16 Bring into action (6)
18 Lovingly (6)
19 Pants (5)

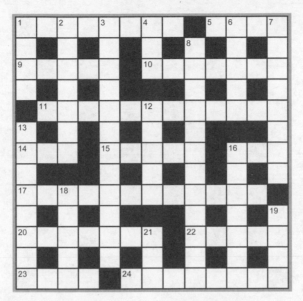

Across

1 Picking (8)
5 One of two equal parts (4)
9 Liquid essential for life (5)
10 Sheikdom in the Persian Gulf (7)
11 Productivity (12)
14 Cheek (slang) (3)
15 Many-headed snake (5)
16 Command to a horse (3)
17 Decide in advance (12)
20 Inactive pill (7)
22 Crevices (5)
23 Clarets (4)
24 Teaches (8)

Down

1 Domestic cattle (4)
2 The exposure of bedrock (7)
3 Uncurled (12)
4 Arrest; apprehend (3)
6 Wide open (of the mouth) (5)
7 Completes a race (8)
8 Devoted to music (12)
12 Type of confection (5)
13 Insect trap (8)
16 Small fast ship (7)
18 Antelope (5)
19 Sues (anag.) (4)
21 Eccentric; strange (3)

CROSSWORD 107

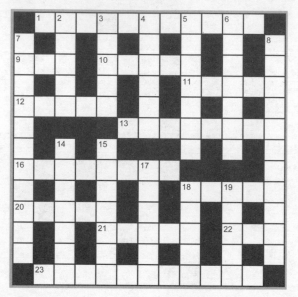

Across

1 Transfer responsibility elsewhere (4,3,4)
9 Make a mistake (3)
10 Bent; bandy (5)
11 Put out a fire (5)
12 More recent (5)
13 Device for spraying paint (8)
16 Irritably (8)
18 Puff up; swell (5)
20 Show triumphant joy (5)
21 Records (5)
22 Charged particle (3)
23 Having celebrities in attendance (4-7)

Down

2 Pointed projectile (5)
3 Grave and serious (5)
4 US state of islands (6)
5 Sum of money owed that cannot be recovered (3,4)
6 Type of cloud (7)
7 Unintelligible (11)
8 Enormous (11)
14 Fractional part (7)
15 Splash (7)
17 Loose part of a garment (6)
18 Beads (anag.) (5)
19 Expect; think that (5)

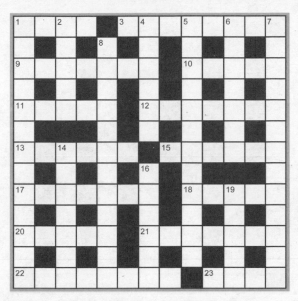

Across

1 Wharf (4)
3 Pleasant scents (8)
9 Set apart (7)
10 Quantitative relation between two amounts (5)
11 Rogue; scoundrel (5)
12 Pass across or through (7)
13 Surpass (6)
15 More likely than not (4-2)
17 Content (7)
18 Greeting (5)
20 Red cosmetic powder (5)
21 Brings about (7)
22 Catastrophe (8)
23 Participate in a game (4)

Down

1 Irascible (5-8)
2 Smell (5)
4 Constructs a building (6)
5 Preservative (12)
6 Type of cell division (7)
7 Impulsively (13)
8 Failure to act with prudence (12)
14 Winged angelic beings (7)
16 Value; respect (6)
19 Nearby (5)

CROSSWORD 109

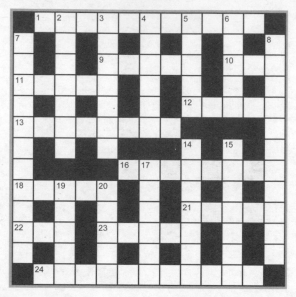

Across

1 Daring; bold (11)
9 Lazy person (5)
10 Farewell remark (3)
11 Alphabetical list (5)
12 Breathing organs (5)
13 Move to another country (8)
16 Increase (8)
18 Conditions (5)
21 Foot joint (5)
22 Seed of an apple (3)
23 Baking appliances (5)
24 Act gloomily (anag.) (11)

Down

2 Contempt (7)
3 Cure-alls (7)
4 Natural skill (6)
5 Rustic (5)
6 Living in a city (5)
7 Huge three-horned dinosaur (11)
8 Quantification (11)
14 Sunshade (7)
15 Supporting (7)
17 Soundless (6)
19 Push back (5)
20 Violent atmospheric disturbance (5)

CROSSWORD 110

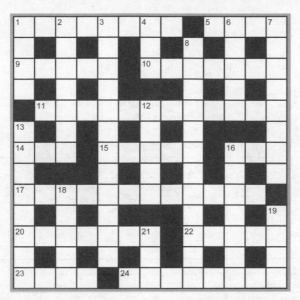

Across

1 Measure of the heat content of a system (8)
5 Church recess (4)
9 Departing (5)
10 Highest vantage point of a building (7)
11 Incessantly (12)
14 Feline (3)
15 Military blockade (5)
16 Enjoyable (3)
17 Made poor (12)
20 Helped to happen (7)
22 Select group of people (5)
23 Fastens a knot (4)
24 Written communications (8)

Down

1 Therefore (Latin) (4)
2 Divide into three parts (7)
3 In a hostile manner (12)
4 Level golf score (3)
6 Ways or tracks (5)
7 Evacuating (8)
8 Despair (12)
12 Belonging to them (5)
13 Mishap (8)
16 Giving food to (7)
18 Shallow circular dish (5)
19 Marries (4)
21 Female kangaroo (3)

CROSSWORD 111

Across

1 Curved shape (4)
3 Imitate (8)
9 Underwater projectile (7)
10 Powerful forward movement (5)
11 Mountain pass (3)
12 Heavy iron block (5)
13 Narrow pieces of land (5)
15 Spoken for (5)
17 ___ Valletta: actress (5)
18 Hip (anag.) (3)
19 Distinguishing characteristic (5)
20 Leaning at an angle (7)
21 Making less clear (8)
22 Extremely (4)

Down

1 Not living up to expectations (13)
2 Christmas song (5)
4 Humorously sarcastic (6)
5 Untimely (12)
6 Act of turning up (7)
7 Eternally (13)
8 Showed (12)
14 Wavering vocal quality (7)
16 Young cat (6)
18 Self-respect (5)

Across

1 Status (4)
3 Sewage discharged into water (8)
9 Mottled (7)
10 Guide a vehicle (5)
11 Someone skilled in penmanship (12)
14 At the present time (3)
16 Type of lizard (5)
17 Drink a little (3)
18 Conflict of opinion (12)
21 Supernatural skill (5)
22 A dancer or singer (7)
23 Fortified wines (8)
24 First man (4)

Down

1 Decreasing (8)
2 Country in the Himalayas (5)
4 Craze (3)
5 Repository for misplaced items (4,8)
6 Small holes in cloth or leather (7)
7 Become weary (4)
8 UFO (6,6)
12 Carer (anag.) (5)
13 Against the current (8)
15 Squirm (7)
19 Became less severe (5)
20 Flightless birds (4)
22 High value playing card (3)

CROSSWORD 113

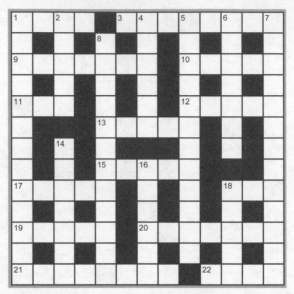

Across

1 Cultivated (4)
3 Leaping over a rope (8)
9 Open area of grassland (7)
10 Cowboy exhibition (5)
11 Unit of energy (3)
12 Poison (5)
13 Bout of extravagant shopping (5)
15 Insect larva (5)
17 Very informal phrases (5)
18 Evergreen coniferous tree (3)
19 Shout of appreciation (5)
20 Provoked; encouraged (7)
21 Stretched out (8)
22 Solely (4)

Down

1 Capable of being understood (13)
2 Strong ringing sound (5)
4 Guardian (6)
5 Firework display (12)
6 Alphabetical lists (7)
7 Amiably (4-9)
8 Scolding (8-4)
14 Anapest (anag.) (7)
16 Ill will (6)
18 Japanese mattress (5)

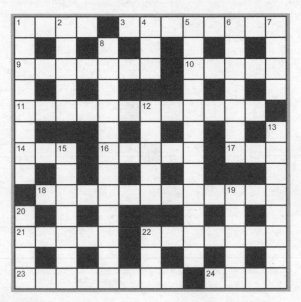

Across

1 Silence (4)
3 Unrealistic (8)
9 Person with auburn hair (7)
10 Strongly advised (5)
11 Act of discussing something; deliberation (12)
14 Long bench (3)
16 Cuban folk dance (5)
17 Word expressing negation (3)
18 Planned in advance (12)
21 Fruit of the oak (5)
22 Flat highland (7)
23 Liked sea (anag.) (8)
24 Perceives with the eyes (4)

Down

1 Printed version of data on a computer (4,4)
2 Carrying chair (5)
4 Assist (3)
5 Military judicial body (5,7)
6 Warning device for ships (7)
7 Removable covers (4)
8 Demands or needs (12)
12 Shy (5)
13 Sports grounds (8)
15 Male witch (7)
19 Subject of a talk (5)
20 Contact by phone (4)
22 Collection of paper (3)

CROSSWORD 115

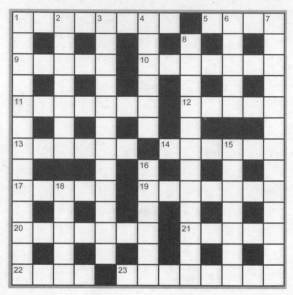

Across

1 Carve words on something (8)
5 Moat (anag.) (4)
9 Crustacean like a shrimp (5)
10 Pals (7)
11 Water-bearing rock (7)
12 Capital of Ghana (5)
13 Of inferior quality (6)
14 Continent (6)
17 Appeal (5)
19 Assign (7)
20 Written language for blind people (7)
21 Visual representation (5)
22 Flat and smooth (4)
23 Most amusing (8)

Down

1 Unfeasible (13)
2 Shoulder blade (7)
3 Not special (3-2-3-4)
4 Opposite of after (6)
6 Invigorating medicine (5)
7 Ineptitude in running a business (13)
8 State of dissatisfaction (12)
15 Copy; mimic (7)
16 Rich cake (6)
18 Ornamental stone (5)

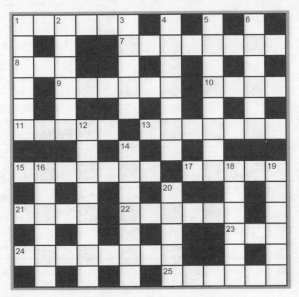

Across

1 Boring; dull (6)
7 Formidable (8)
8 Vessel; jolt (3)
9 Of the eye (6)
10 Snake-like fish (4)
11 Trail (5)
13 Green vegetation (7)
15 Thing causing outrage (7)
17 Scheme intended to deceive (3-2)
21 Colliery (4)
22 Tropical fruit (6)
23 Month (3)
24 Grandiosity of language (8)
25 Snores (anag.) (6)

Down

1 Dispirit (6)
2 Moon of the planet Jupiter (6)
3 Give up (5)
4 Stimulated; urged on (7)
5 Bring together (8)
6 Remove an obstruction from a sink (6)
12 Religious residences (8)
14 Meddles with (7)
16 Trite remark (6)
18 Walks heavily and firmly (6)
19 Participant in a game (6)
20 Glasses (abbrev.) (5)

CROSSWORD 117

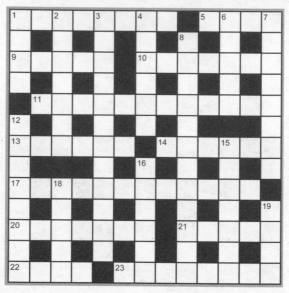

Across

1 Open resistance (8)
5 Adjoin (4)
9 Pertaining to the sun (5)
10 Country in western Africa (7)
11 Poorly fed (12)
13 Set in layers (6)
14 Book of accounts (6)
17 Excessive stress (12)
20 Welcomed (7)
21 Data entered into a system (5)
22 Spool-like toy (4)
23 Cut across (8)

Down

1 Fine powder (4)
2 Decorated with leaves (7)
3 Agreements; plans (12)
4 Hardened part of the skin (6)
6 Hard close-grained wood (5)
7 Back and forth (2,3,3)
8 Destruction (12)
12 Powerfully (8)
15 Quick look (7)
16 Arachnid (6)
18 Military opponent (5)
19 Proofreader's mark meaning 'let it stand' (4)

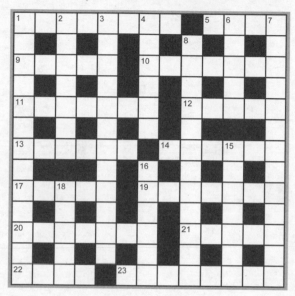

Across

1 Second month (8)
5 Group of countries in an alliance (4)
9 Targeted (5)
10 Widen (7)
11 Receiver (7)
12 Arduous search for something (5)
13 Country (6)
14 One's environment (6)
17 Divide in two (5)
19 Active part of a fire (7)
20 Upstart; one who has recently gained wealth (7)
21 Wild dog of Australia (5)
22 Less than average tide (4)
23 Dishes that begin a meal (8)

Down

1 A transient occurrence (5,2,3,3)
2 Pompous language (7)
3 Not found (12)
4 Automata (6)
6 Shelf (5)
7 Buildings (13)
8 Spanish adventurer (12)
15 Encroach (7)
16 Push forcefully (6)
18 Insect grub (5)

CROSSWORD 119

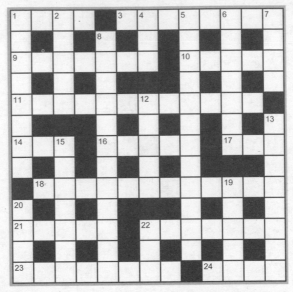

Across

1 Mocks (4)
3 Medieval weapon (8)
9 Disagreement (7)
10 Religious acts (5)
11 Menacing (12)
14 Of recent origin (3)
16 Works one's trade steadily (5)
17 Sound of a dove (3)
18 Orcas (6,6)
21 Prevent (5)
22 Very long lasting (7)
23 Right to self-government (8)
24 Money given to the poor (4)

Down

1 Massive luminous star (3,5)
2 Beets (anag.) (5)
4 Fishing stick (3)
5 Atmospheric layer (12)
6 Pertaining to plants (7)
7 Cardinal point (4)
8 Worldly (12)
12 Less moist (5)
13 Fictional ugly creatures (8)
15 Palest (7)
19 Published false statement (5)
20 Mother (4)
22 Water barrier (3)

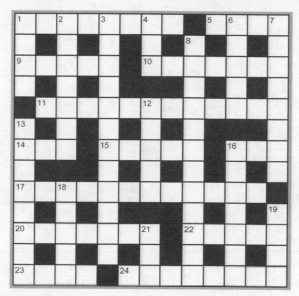

Across

1 Cunning; contrivance (8)
5 From a distance (4)
9 Very foolish (5)
10 Leftovers (7)
11 Generally accepted (12)
14 Nocturnal bird of prey (3)
15 Captivates (5)
16 Male person (3)
17 Sweet red fruits (12)
20 Makes a continuous deep sound (7)
22 Illegal payment (5)
23 Freedom from difficulty or hardship (4)
24 Physical power (8)

Down

1 Helper; assistant (4)
2 Average (7)
3 Unseen observer (3,2,3,4)
4 Mongrel dog (3)
6 Throw forcefully (5)
7 Living in (8)
8 Limitless (12)
12 Tower (anag.) (5)
13 Interpret in a certain way (8)
16 Assembly of people (7)
18 Slopes (5)
19 Wire lattice (4)
21 Posed (3)

CROSSWORD 121

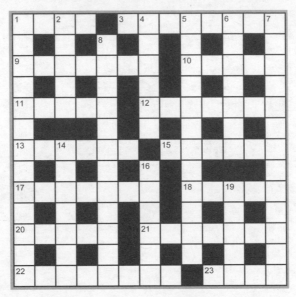

Across

1 Very small quantity (4)
3 Country in the Indian Ocean (8)
9 Flowers with white petals (7)
10 Device for sharpening razors (5)
11 Big cat (5)
12 More foolish (7)
13 List of ingredients for a dish (6)
15 Roll of parchment (6)
17 Fatuously (7)
18 Saying; slogan (5)
20 Passageway (5)
21 Those who catch prey (7)
22 Boating (8)
23 In a tense state (4)

Down

1 Vagueness (13)
2 Unspecified object (5)
4 Support (6)
5 Misplaced net (anag.) (12)
6 Fear of heights (7)
7 In a manner that exceeds
  what is necessary (13)
8 Give a false account of (12)
14 Traditional example (7)
16 Large snake (6)
19 Walk (5)

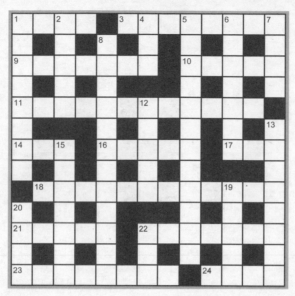

Across

1 Cunning (4)
3 Sample for medical testing (8)
9 Not tense (7)
10 Relating to Norway (5)
11 Blends; mixtures (12)
14 Helpful hint (3)
16 Welcome (5)
17 Drowned river valley (3)
18 Dimly; not clearly (12)
21 Sandy wasteland (5)
22 West Indian musical style (7)
23 Garment worn after a shower (8)
24 Decorated a cake (4)

Down

1 Savage fierceness (8)
2 Vascular tissue in plants (5)
4 Group of whales (3)
5 Constantly; always (12)
6 Sailor (7)
7 Negative votes (4)
8 Device for putting out fires (12)
12 Wide-awake (5)
13 Infancy (8)
15 Tapering flag (7)
19 Theme for a discussion (5)
20 Freshwater game fish (4)
22 Edible nut (3)

CROSSWORD 123

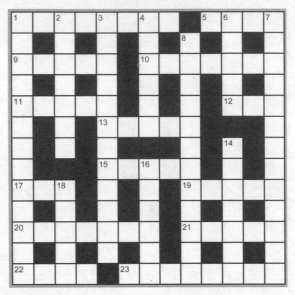

Across

1 Paintings (8)
5 Encourage in wrongdoing (4)
9 Cram (5)
10 Intrusions (7)
11 Bring on oneself (5)
12 Bind (3)
13 Fit with glass (5)
15 Urns (5)
17 Annoy (3)
19 Effigies (5)
20 Perfectly (7)
21 Prod with the elbow (5)
22 Locate or place (4)
23 Introductory pieces of music (8)

Down

1 Things that may happen (13)
2 A governing body in a county (7)
3 Not excusable (12)
4 Mystery; riddle (6)
6 Brag (5)
7 Blandness (13)
8 Opposite of amateur (12)
14 Packed (7)
16 Woodcutter (6)
18 Went down on one knee (5)

CROSSWORD 124

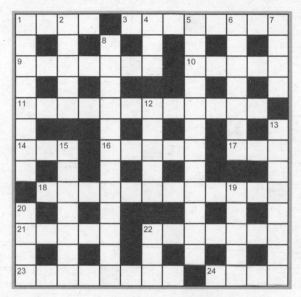

Across

1 Too; in addition (4)
3 Sell at a lower price (8)
9 Abounding (7)
10 Smoothed one's nails (5)
11 Uncomplimentary (12)
14 Large salt water body (3)
16 Recycle (5)
17 False statement (3)
18 Regardless of (12)
21 Skewered meat (5)
22 Open air controlled blaze (7)
23 Ragged (8)
24 In an inactive way; with no particular purpose (4)

Down

1 Unselfish concern for others (8)
2 Projecting horizontal ledge (5)
4 Annoy continuously (3)
5 Bubbling (12)
6 Rank in the forces (7)
7 Clean up (4)
8 Unpleasant (12)
12 Solid blow (5)
13 Acutely (8)
15 Performer of gymnastic feats (7)
19 Epic poem ascribed to Homer (5)
20 Comedy sketch (4)
22 Insect which collects pollen (3)

CROSSWORD 125

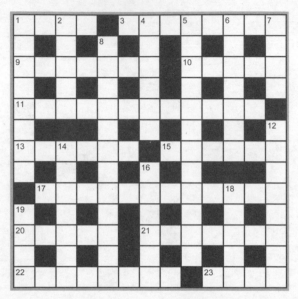

Across

1 Pass the tongue over (4)
3 Sailing swiftly (8)
9 Master of ceremonies (7)
10 Grasslike marsh plant (5)
11 Informally (12)
13 Nearer (anag.) (6)
15 Where one finds Athens (6)
17 The ? symbol (8,4)
20 Confuse (5)
21 Capital of the US state of Georgia (7)
22 Bogs or marshes (8)
23 Scarpered (4)

Down

1 University teacher (8)
2 Brief appearance (5)
4 Close tightly (6)
5 Hopelessly (12)
6 Satisfy a desire (7)
7 Departs (4)
8 Altruism (12)
12 Crew member (on a ship) (8)
14 More circular (7)
16 Conclusion (6)
18 Cancel (5)
19 Use land for growing crops (4)

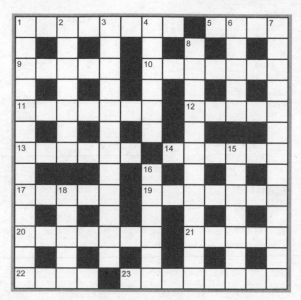

Across

1 Where one parks the car (8)
5 At any time (4)
9 Unsuitable (5)
10 Capital of Kenya (7)
11 Pertaining to the tongue (7)
12 Finely cut straw (5)
13 Of the universe (6)
14 Deer horn (6)
17 Killer whales (5)
19 Official proving of a will (7)
20 Japanese dish of raw fish (7)
21 Lessen (5)
22 Repeat (4)
23 Footpath for pedestrians (8)

Down

1 Betrayer (6-7)
2 Young children (7)
3 Very eager; keen (12)
4 Declares invalid (6)
6 Musical instrument (5)
7 Action of strengthening (13)
8 Very sad (12)
15 Discharge from a hole in a pipe (7)
16 Top aim (anag.) (6)
18 Enclosed (5)

CROSSWORD 127

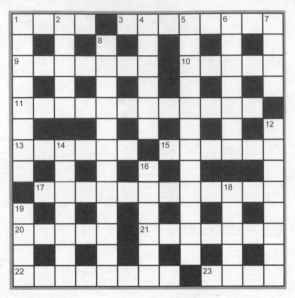

Across

1 Tax (4)
3 Two-wheeled vehicles (8)
9 Conspire to commit a fraud (7)
10 Conceal (5)
11 Act of sending a message (12)
13 Standard; usual (6)
15 Remains preserved in rock (6)
17 Chatter (6-6)
20 Stadium (5)
21 Material such as gravel (7)
22 Extremely accomplished (8)
23 Refuse to admit (4)

Down

1 Finding (8)
2 Roman country house (5)
4 Religious leader (6)
5 Now and then (12)
6 Jealous (7)
7 Put in order (4)
8 Strengthen; confirm (12)
12 Eloquently (8)
14 People who attack at speed (7)
16 Oral (6)
18 Make fun of someone (5)
19 Soothing ointment (4)

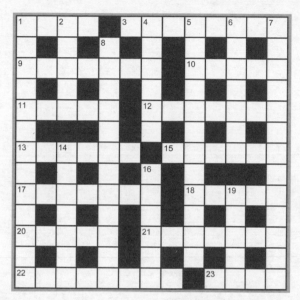

Across

1 Tall cereal grass (4)
3 Ocean (8)
9 Pasta strips (7)
10 Show-off (5)
11 Avoid (5)
12 Ugly building (7)
13 Irrelevant pieces of information (6)
15 Gather or collect (4,2)
17 Stinted (anag.) (7)
18 Symbol (5)
20 Excess (5)
21 Remove a difficulty (7)
22 Abruptly (8)
23 Small pointed missile (4)

Down

1 Satisfaction (13)
2 Dry red wine (5)
4 Throws a coin in the air (6)
5 Showing gratitude (12)
6 Grassy clump (7)
7 Person who writes letters regularly (13)
8 Unlawful (12)
14 Caused to catch fire (7)
16 Walk casually (6)
19 Australian marsupial (5)

CROSSWORD 129

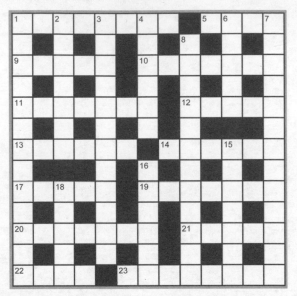

Across

1 Separate; disconnected (8)
5 Anti-aircraft fire (4)
9 Compel (5)
10 The Windy City (7)
11 Demanded (7)
12 Path to follow (5)
13 Change gradually (6)
14 In truth; really (6)
17 Bird claw (5)
19 Settle a dispute (7)
20 At the ocean floor (7)
21 Ascend (5)
22 What you hear with (4)
23 Impressive manner of a person (8)

Down

1 Distinguish between (13)
2 Cyclone (7)
3 Inventiveness (12)
4 Encrypt (6)
6 Camel-like animal (5)
7 Intelligent and informed (13)
8 Easy targets (7,5)
15 Avoidance (7)
16 Marble (anag.) (6)
18 Stratum (5)

CROSSWORD 130

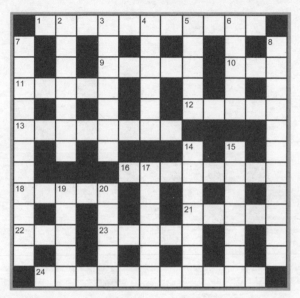

Across

1 Pertaining to office workers (5-6)
9 Hurled (5)
10 Cooking appliance (3)
11 Breathe in audibly (5)
12 Opposite of a winner (5)
13 Rigorous appraisal (4,4)
16 Highly seasoned smoked beef (8)
18 Singing voices (5)
21 Respond to (5)
22 Foot extremity (3)
23 Brown earth pigment (5)
24 Watching over one's flock (11)

Down

2 Taxonomic group including humans (7)
3 Silklike fabric (7)
4 Where tennis and squash are played (6)
5 Allowed by official rules (5)
6 Cinders (5)
7 Eating establishments (11)
8 Shortened (11)
14 Set in motion; agitated (7)
15 Marmoset (7)
17 Fit for cultivation (of land) (6)
19 E.g. incisors and molars (5)
20 Drink noisily (5)

CROSSWORD 131

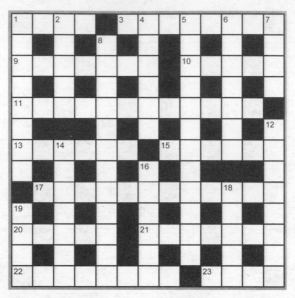

Across

1 Abstain from food (4)
3 Substance that speeds up a reaction (8)
9 People who make money (7)
10 Gave out playing cards (5)
11 Extremely weakening (12)
13 Safe (6)
15 Stiff and stilted (6)
17 Sound of quick light steps (6-6)
20 Japanese form of fencing (5)
21 Greet (7)
22 Disciplined (8)
23 Midge (4)

Down

1 Diabolically cruel (8)
2 Cleanse by rubbing (5)
4 Items of value (6)
5 And also (12)
6 Longed for (7)
7 Young children (4)
8 Formal announcements (12)
12 Most annoyed (8)
14 Sophisticated hairstyle (7)
16 Look through casually (6)
18 Plant spike (5)
19 Bypass (4)

Across

1 Publisher's emblem (8)
5 Protective foot covering (4)
9 Scoundrel (5)
10 Japanese flower arranging (7)
11 Undo (5)
12 Droop (3)
13 Facial protuberances (5)
15 Dreadful (5)
17 Small social insect (3)
19 Jump over (5)
20 Write music (7)
21 Wanderer (5)
22 Neither good nor bad (2-2)
23 Furtive (8)

Down

1 The facts surrounding an event (13)
2 Illuminate (5,2)
3 Formal introduction (12)
4 Repulsive (6)
6 Piles (5)
7 In an inflated manner (13)
8 State of the USA (12)
14 Drop sharply (7)
16 Articulate; eloquent (6)
18 Domesticates (5)

CROSSWORD 133

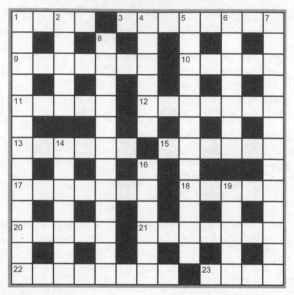

Across

1 Fall vertically (4)
3 State capital of Ohio (8)
9 Move like a snake (7)
10 Triangular river mouth (5)
11 Relating to the kidneys (5)
12 Miserly person (7)
13 Award (6)
15 Notable inconvenience (6)
17 Aromatic herb (7)
18 Creates (5)
20 Detailed financial assessment (5)
21 Single eyeglass (7)
22 Submissive (8)
23 Small vipers (4)

Down

1 Carry editions (anag.) (13)
2 The Hunter (constellation) (5)
4 Female monster (6)
5 Clothing such as a vest (12)
6 Fat or bulging (7)
7 Brazenness (13)
8 Showing total commitment (12)
14 Late (7)
16 Archer (6)
19 Strikes with the foot (5)

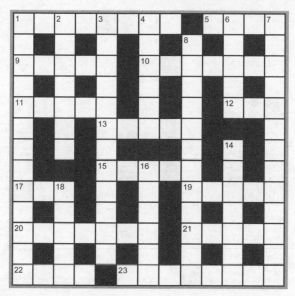

Across

1 Simplified drawings (8)
5 Indian dress (4)
9 Waterlogged ground (5)
10 Decline gradually (4-3)
11 Leaves (5)
12 Our star (3)
13 Flower part; pales (anag.) (5)
15 Go away from quickly (5)
17 Young bear (3)
19 Borders (5)
20 220 yards (7)
21 Self-evident truth (5)
22 Thin strip of wood (4)
23 Postponement (8)

Down

1 Rude (13)
2 Greed (7)
3 Reclamation (12)
4 Fictional (4,2)
6 Basic units of an element (5)
7 Extremely small (13)
8 Bring together into a mass (12)
14 More irate (7)
16 Style of popular music (6)
18 Destroyed by fire (5)

CROSSWORD 135

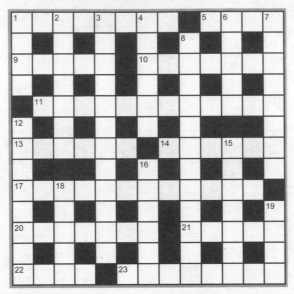

Across

1 Conduct business (8)
5 Male sheep (pl.) (4)
9 Brilliant (5)
10 Precipitating (7)
11 Grandeur (12)
13 Capital of Canada (6)
14 Arthropod (6)
17 Changes to a situation (12)
20 Last longer than others (of clothes) (7)
21 Armistice (5)
22 Ride the waves (4)
23 E.g. hats and helmets (8)

Down

1 Throw a coin in the air (4)
2 Road or roofing material (7)
3 Determined (6-6)
4 Glass container (6)
6 Pertaining to bees (5)
7 Implies (8)
8 Unplugged (12)
12 Awesome (8)
15 Speak excitedly of (7)
16 Not dense (6)
18 Elector (5)
19 Cry of derision (4)

Across

1 Huge (8)
5 Chickens lay these (4)
9 Golf shots (5)
10 Decorative altar cloth (7)
11 Implant (5)
12 Small legume (3)
13 Personal attendant (5)
15 Anxious (5)
17 Belonging to us (3)
19 In what place (5)
20 Endanger (7)
21 Skirmish (5)
22 Look or manner (4)
23 Mesmerism (8)

Down

1 Art movement (13)
2 Tenth month (7)
3 Mishap (12)
4 Unfold (6)
6 Rise to one's feet (3,2)
7 Conscious knowledge of oneself (4-9)
8 Female fellow national (12)
14 Hassles; prickles (7)
16 Actually (6)
18 Indian monetary unit (5)

CROSSWORD 137

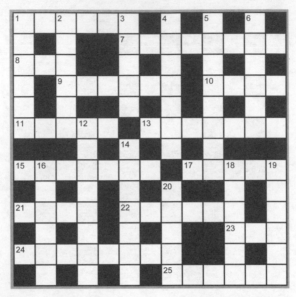

Across

1 Makes spick and span (6)
7 Pertaining to the arts (8)
8 Strong drink (3)
9 Loves dearly (6)
10 Suggestion or tip (4)
11 Card game (5)
13 Listening (7)
15 Walk with difficulty (7)
17 Snake (5)
21 Slender woody shoot (4)
22 Demands; insists on (6)
23 Toothed wheel (3)
24 Wave or flourish a weapon (8)
25 Absorbent cloths (6)

Down

1 Arrive (4,2)
2 Table linen; woven fabric (6)
3 Open disrespect (5)
4 These aid sight (7)
5 Elation (8)
6 Substance found in wine (6)
12 Pleasing and captivating (8)
14 Nonconformist (7)
16 Oppose a plan successfully (6)
18 Mistake in snooker; blunder (6)
19 Sayings (6)
20 Sailing vessel (5)

CROSSWORD 138

Across

1 Soft leather shoe (8)
5 Shut with force (4)
9 Shine brightly (5)
10 Needleworker (7)
11 Exceptional (12)
14 What you hear with (3)
15 Parody (5)
16 Silent (3)
17 Comprehensive (3-9)
20 One who finds water by dowsing (7)
22 Pertaining to birth (5)
23 Dreadful (4)
24 Thinks about something continually (8)

Down

1 Foolish people (informal) (4)
2 Easier to understand (7)
3 Firm rebuke (12)
4 Kind or sort (3)
6 Type of coffee drink (5)
7 Nautical (8)
8 Importance (12)
12 Group of singers (5)
13 Insisted upon (8)
16 Periods of 60 seconds (7)
18 Revel (anag.) (5)
19 European mountain range (4)
21 Mock (3)

CROSSWORD 139

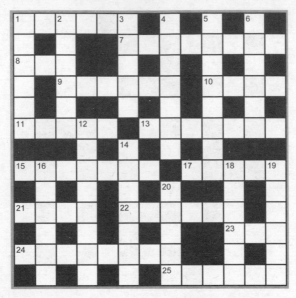

Across

1 Domed roof (6)
7 Make more light (8)
8 North American nation (abbrev.) (3)
9 Representation of a concept; diagram (6)
10 Semiaquatic mammal (4)
11 Long for (5)
13 Remains of living things (7)
15 Listeners (7)
17 Common edible fruit (5)
21 Big cat (4)
22 Celestial body (6)
23 Edge of a cup (3)
24 A large spar (8)
25 Fanatic (6)

Down

1 Brusque and irritable (6)
2 State of matter (6)
3 Monastery church (5)
4 Deny any responsibility for (7)
5 Sign of approval (6-2)
6 Plant of the parsley family (6)
12 Scarceness (8)
14 Sparred (anag.) (7)
16 The boss at a newspaper (6)
18 Keep watch over an area (6)
19 Absolve (6)
20 Ballroom dance (5)

Across

1 Hot and humid (8)
5 Mark left from a wound (4)
9 Smallest quantity (5)
10 Belief that there is no God (7)
11 Type of tooth (5)
12 Place (3)
13 Piece of code to automate a task (5)
15 Remove errors from software (5)
17 Female sheep (3)
19 Mortal (5)
20 Resistance to change (7)
21 Performer (5)
22 Lesion (4)
23 Intellectual (8)

Down

1 Advertising by telephone (13)
2 Prophets (7)
3 Coming between two things in time (12)
4 Middle Eastern language (6)
6 Bend or curl (5)
7 Device for changing TV channel (6,7)
8 Street (12)
14 Gnawing animal (7)
16 Tell off severely (6)
18 Levels out (5)

CROSSWORD **141**

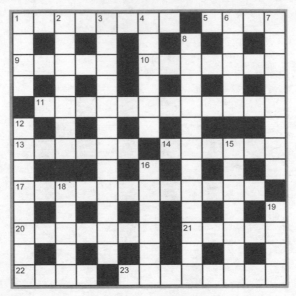

Across

1 Support you can lean against (8)
5 Therefore (4)
9 Marrying man (5)
10 Massage technique (7)
11 Thriftily (12)
13 Series of prayers (6)
14 Call for the presence of (6)
17 Building (12)
20 Evident (7)
21 Take place; happen (5)
22 Fine soft thread (4)
23 Search for minerals (8)

Down

1 Listening devices (4)
2 Options (7)
3 Money paid for work (12)
4 Plant with oil rich seeds (6)
6 Place providing accommodation (5)
7 Reading carefully (8)
8 Ill-mannered (12)
12 Of great value (8)
15 Shackle (7)
16 One who manages finances at a college (6)
18 Pertaining to warships (5)
19 Backbone; fortitude (4)

CROSSWORD 142

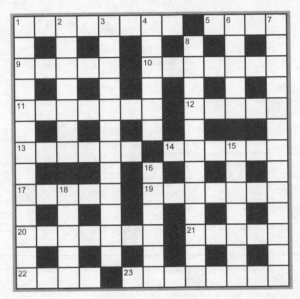

Across

1 Mean sect (anag.) (8)
5 Retail store (4)
9 Humming (5)
10 Grapple with (7)
11 Writers (7)
12 Group of activists (5)
13 Intense fear (6)
14 Exertion (6)
17 Wanderer (5)
19 Type of porch (7)
20 Friendly understanding (7)
21 Sour substances (5)
22 Be in a huff (4)
23 Hard work (8)

Down

1 Dull and uninteresting (13)
2 Walk leisurely (7)
3 Female singing voice (5-7)
4 Freshest (6)
6 Despised (5)
7 Affectedly (13)
8 From this time on (12)
15 Aperture or hole (7)
16 Raise up (6)
18 Essential (5)

CROSSWORD 143

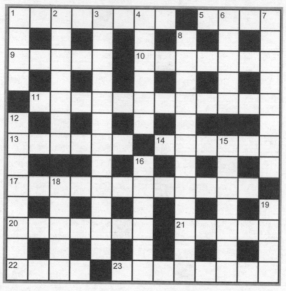

Across

1 Great energy; vitality (8)
5 Clothing (4)
9 Praise enthusiastically (5)
10 In the middle (7)
11 Not on purpose (12)
13 Military decorations (6)
14 Coarse cloth (6)
17 Teach to accept a belief uncritically (12)
20 Voted in to office (7)
21 Long wooden seat (5)
22 Mission (4)
23 Turns around (8)

Down

1 Rode (anag.) (4)
2 Observed (7)
3 A large number (12)
4 Holy (6)
6 Fourth month (5)
7 Extravagant fuss (8)
8 Impossible to achieve (12)
12 Impending (8)
15 Plans to do something (7)
16 Hold gently and carefully (6)
18 Put clothes on (5)
19 Reasons; explanations (4)

CROSSWORD 144

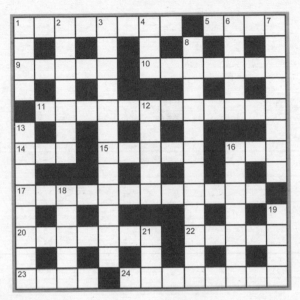

Across

1 Truthfulness (8)
5 Look at amorously (4)
9 Arboreal primate (5)
10 Seed bid (anag.) (7)
11 Formal notice (12)
14 Single in number (3)
15 Bolt for fastening metal plates (5)
16 Argument against something (3)
17 Sweat (12)
20 Triangle with three unequal sides (7)
22 Possessed (5)
23 Quantity of medication (4)
24 Sweet food courses (8)

Down

1 SI unit of electromotive force (4)
2 Love; genre of fiction (7)
3 Mapmaker (12)
4 Key on a computer keyboard (3)
6 Objection; complain (5)
7 Throwing out (8)
8 Coming from outside (12)
12 Not at all (5)
13 Serene and assured (8)
16 Singer (7)
18 Calls out like a lion (5)
19 Increases; sums up (4)
21 First woman (3)

CROSSWORD 145

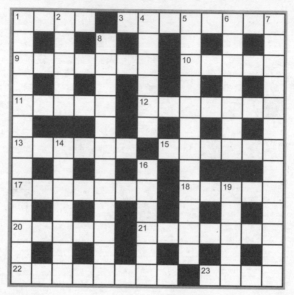

Across

1 Widespread (4)
3 Reverie (8)
9 River of southeastern Africa (7)
10 Move (5)
11 Made a mistake (5)
12 Religious sacrament (7)
13 Customer (6)
15 Large eel (6)
17 Make less intense (7)
18 Horse's cry (5)
20 Try out (5)
21 Frees from an obligation (7)
22 Official list of names (8)
23 Sight organs (4)

Down

1 Amusement park ride (6,7)
2 Thigh bone (5)
4 Single-celled organism (6)
5 Feeling let down (12)
6 Going out (7)
7 Process of transformation
  (of an insect) (13)
8 Birds of prey (6,6)
14 Distributing (7)
16 Withdraw (6)
19 State indirectly (5)

CROSSWORD 146

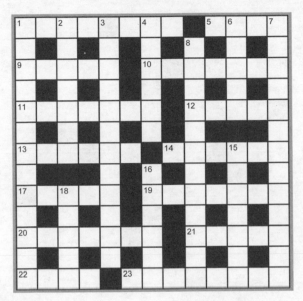

Across

1 Large rocks (8)
5 Tiny parasite (4)
9 Pungent edible bulb (5)
10 Holy place (7)
11 Enunciate (7)
12 Trembling poplar (5)
13 Continue to exist (6)
14 Isolationists (6)
17 Quilt (5)
19 Constructor (7)
20 Platform projecting from a wall (7)
21 Game fish (5)
22 Saw; observed (4)
23 Teacher (8)

Down

1 Capable of being decomposed (13)
2 Identifying outfit (7)
3 Condemnation (12)
4 Uttered coarsely (6)
6 Abatement (5)
7 Person who manages the affairs of an insolvent company (13)
8 Unfriendly (12)
15 Last in a series (7)
16 Complied with orders (6)
18 Regard highly (5)

CROSSWORD 147

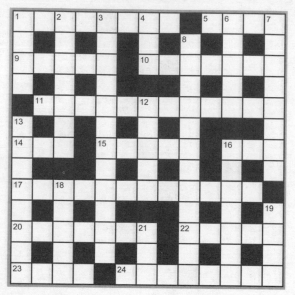

Across

1 Stops temporarily (8)
5 Type of air pollution (4)
9 Collection of ships (5)
10 Vessel that cleans rivers (7)
11 Make a guess that is too high (12)
14 Possessed (3)
15 In front (5)
16 Very small child (3)
17 Astonishing; amazing (3-9)
20 Paired (7)
22 Remnant of a dying fire (5)
23 Tiny specks (4)
24 Totally clean (8)

Down

1 Settee (4)
2 Abandoned a plan (7)
3 Amusing (12)
4 Performed an action (3)
6 Hot rock (5)
7 Items of clothing (8)
8 Total confusion (12)
12 Engross oneself in (5)
13 Frustrated (8)
16 Plausible; defensible (7)
18 Be alive; be real (5)
19 Part of the eye (4)
21 Depression (3)

CROSSWORD 148

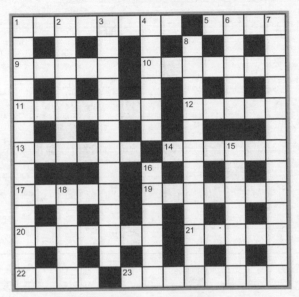

Across

1 Sunshades (8)
5 Long poem (4)
9 Religious table (5)
10 Perfect happiness (7)
11 Slender stemlike plant appendage (7)
12 Not illuminated (5)
13 Wrinkle (6)
14 Sagacity (6)
17 Unit of light (5)
19 Involving active participation (5-2)
20 Conceals something from view (7)
21 Reluctant (5)
22 Greek god of love (4)
23 Rubbish (8)

Down

1 Playful trick (9,4)
2 Group of assistants (7)
3 Shockingly (12)
4 Missing human interaction (6)
6 Jewel from an oyster shell (5)
7 Artisanship (13)
8 A type of error in speech (8,4)
15 Feeling of hopelessness (7)
16 Long-bladed hand tool (6)
18 Very masculine (5)

CROSSWORD 149

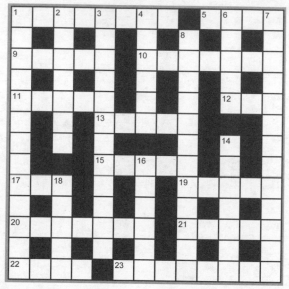

Across

1 Sprightliness; eagerness (8)
5 Proper (4)
9 Cash registers (5)
10 Long-bladed hand tools (7)
11 Lumberjack (5)
12 Pronoun used to refer to a ship (3)
13 Happen again (5)
15 Ape (abbrev.) (5)
17 Trouble in body or mind (3)
19 Place of refuge (5)
20 Annoying (7)
21 Stringed instrument (5)
22 Movement of water causing a small whirlpool (4)
23 Fills with air (8)

Down

1 Medication for allergies (13)
2 Permitted (7)
3 Revival of something (12)
4 Plan; strategy (6)
6 Rushes (5)
7 Of mixed character (13)
8 Pertaining to a person's life (12)
14 Brook (7)
16 Confine as a prisoner (6)
18 Found agreeable (5)

CROSSWORD 150

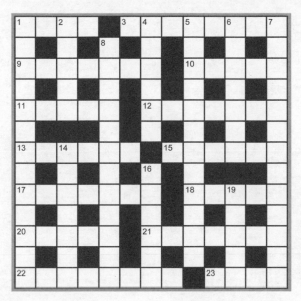

Across

- **1** Skin irritation (4)
- **3** Happened (8)
- **9** Seize and take custody of (7)
- **10** Talons (5)
- **11** Cease being awake (5)
- **12** Restrained (7)
- **13** Most pleasant (6)
- **15** Spanish festival (6)
- **17** Tranquil (7)
- **18** Change; modify (5)
- **20** Fabric with parallel ribs (5)
- **21** Vexing (7)
- **22** Transporting by hand (8)
- **23** Stock of money (4)

Down

- **1** Peculiar or individual (13)
- **2** Small woodland (5)
- **4** Treat indulgently (6)
- **5** Unkind; unsympathetic (12)
- **6** Attains (7)
- **7** Deprived (13)
- **8** Resolutely (12)
- **14** Teller (7)
- **16** Catchphrase (6)
- **19** Word of farewell (5)

CROSSWORD 151

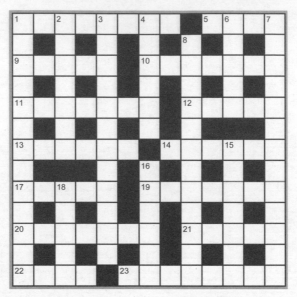

Across

1 Unproven (8)
5 Propel the body through water (4)
9 Speak without preparation (2-3)
10 Skill (7)
11 Laconic (anag.) (7)
12 Longest river in Europe (5)
13 Believer in the occult (6)
14 Steal; seize suddenly (6)
17 Dole out (5)
19 Joins together (7)
20 Not outside (7)
21 Period of darkness (5)
22 Fixed costs (4)
23 Announces formally (8)

Down

1 Alone (13)
2 Skills (7)
3 Advance payment (12)
4 Gets rid of (6)
6 Round steering device (5)
7 State of the USA (13)
8 In accordance with general custom (12)
15 Part of a gun (7)
16 Chase (6)
18 Small house (5)

CROSSWORD 152

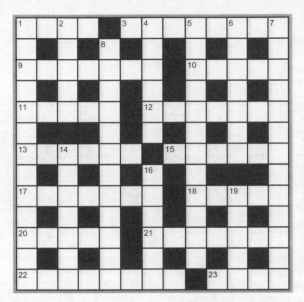

Across

1 Pack down tightly (4)
3 Importance; stress (8)
9 Alongside each other (7)
10 More pleasant (5)
11 Spirit of the air (5)
12 Need (7)
13 Domains (6)
15 Is unable to (6)
17 Scrape (7)
18 Tease or pester (5)
20 Type of chemical bond (5)
21 Hot wind blowing from northern Africa (7)
22 Goading; teasing (8)
23 Short pins that taper at one end (4)

Down

1 Violation of a law (13)
2 Ethical (5)
4 Things that impart motion (6)
5 Squint harder (anag.) (12)
6 Subdivision (7)
7 Clandestine (13)
8 Relating to numbers (12)
14 Place in order (7)
16 Selected (6)
19 Male relation (5)

CROSSWORD 153

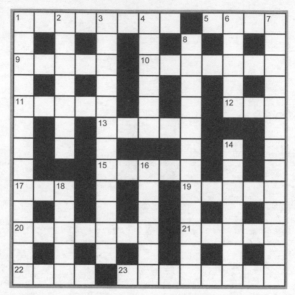

Across

1 Crafty; cunning (8)
5 Hero (4)
9 Large fruit with pulpy flesh (5)
10 Combining (7)
11 Precipice (5)
12 Stomach (3)
13 Behaved (5)
15 Absorbent cloth (5)
17 Domestic bovine animal (3)
19 In the company of (5)
20 Weigh down (7)
21 Sweet substance (5)
22 Soft drink (US) (4)
23 Unequal (3-5)

Down

1 Partially awake (13)
2 Stopping (7)
3 Maker (12)
4 Type of confectionery (6)
6 Performing a deed (5)
7 Prone to steal (5-8)
8 Binoculars (5,7)
14 Treated unjustly (7)
16 Owners (anag.) (6)
18 Erased (5)

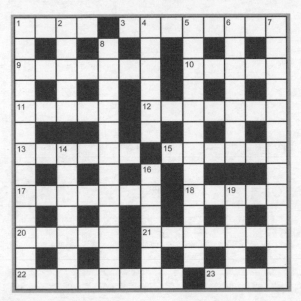

Across

1 Shout loudly; howl (4)
3 Continues obstinately (8)
9 Human-like robot (7)
10 Customary (5)
11 Principle or belief (5)
12 Slim (7)
13 Involving financial matters (6)
15 Small pet canine (6)
17 Dissimilar (7)
18 Act of stealing (5)
20 Glazed earthenware (5)
21 Spicy Spanish sausage (7)
22 In these times (8)
23 Insects that make honey (4)

Down

1 Animal used for heavy work (5,2,6)
2 Broaden (5)
4 First born (6)
5 Bewilderment (12)
6 Sped along; skimmed (7)
7 Sanctimonious (4-9)
8 Showed not to be true (12)
14 Swift-flying songbird (7)
16 Fine; great (6)
19 Expulsion from a country (5)

CROSSWORD 155

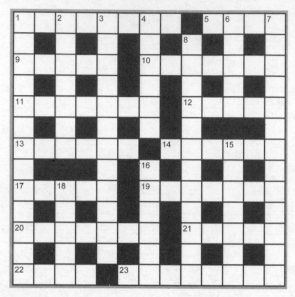

Across

1 Quarter note (8)
5 Devastation (4)
9 Noble gas (5)
10 Large number (7)
11 Conquered by force (7)
12 Inexpensive (5)
13 Interruption of service (6)
14 Type of nursery (6)
17 Anxiety (5)
19 Tallest species of penguin (7)
20 Irreligious (7)
21 Film directed by Ridley Scott (5)
22 Protuberance on a plant (4)
23 Form the base for (8)

Down

1 Confirmation (13)
2 Remnant (7)
3 Gathering of people (12)
4 Fur of a stoat or weasel (6)
6 Join together (5)
7 Absence (13)
8 Coat with a metal (12)
15 Squash (7)
16 Period of instruction (6)
18 Looked at open-mouthed (5)

CROSSWORD 156

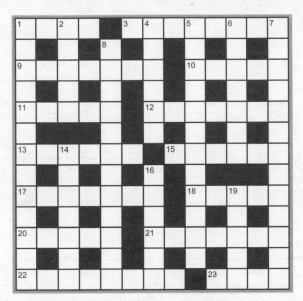

Across

1 Unattractive (4)
3 Exclamation of surprise (8)
9 Variety of rummy (7)
10 Express one's opinion (5)
11 Perhaps (5)
12 Listless (7)
13 Paths of electrons around nuclei (6)
15 Swiss city (6)
17 Become tense (7)
18 Impair (5)
20 Small tuned drum (5)
21 First light (7)
22 Passing (of time) (8)
23 Exhausts; plant fluids (4)

Down

1 Uneasy (13)
2 Tall and thin (5)
4 By word of mouth (6)
5 Germicide (12)
6 Person moved from danger (7)
7 Loyalty in the face of trouble (13)
8 Intended to attract notice (12)
14 Plant with bright flowers (7)
16 Agreement or concord (6)
19 Balearic party island (5)

CROSSWORD 157

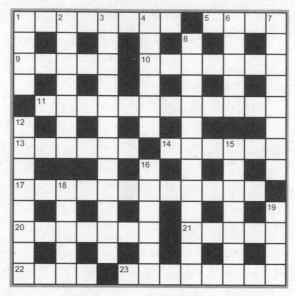

Across
1 State of remaining alive (8)
5 Simple non-flowering plant (4)
9 Having three dimensions (5)
10 The small details of something (7)
11 Brusque and surly (12)
13 Pokes gently (6)
14 Third sign of the zodiac (6)
17 Precondition (12)
20 Coiffure (7)
21 Utter impulsively (5)
22 Skirt worn by ballerinas (4)
23 Foliage (8)

Down
1 Foot covering (4)
2 Ricochet (7)
3 Ineptness (12)
4 Fleet of ships (6)
6 Language of the Romans (5)
7 Icy natal (anag.) (8)
8 Not capable of justification (12)
12 Photograph (8)
15 Trespass (7)
16 This is spread on toast (6)
18 Announcement (5)
19 Remain in the same place (4)

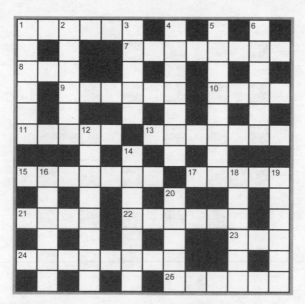

Across

1 Type of ski race (6)
7 Person who leaves a country (8)
8 Wander aimlessly (3)
9 Horizontal supporting beam (6)
10 Precious metal (4)
11 Ye old (anag.) (5)
13 Official language of Britain (7)
15 Concludes by reasoning (7)
17 Sacred hymn or song (5)
21 Molten matter (4)
22 Sharp pain (6)
23 Male sheep (3)
24 Pennant (8)
25 Trying experience (6)

Down

1 Sweet (6)
2 Mixed up or confused (6)
3 E.g. beef and lamb (5)
4 Using great physical force (7)
5 Writhes like a worm (8)
6 Fishes (6)
12 Copied (8)
14 Hour of going to sleep (7)
16 Plays out (6)
18 Strongly opposed (6)
19 E.g. monkey or whale (6)
20 Extremely small (prefix) (5)

CROSSWORD 159

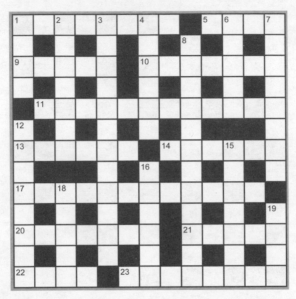

Across

1 Plummet (8)
5 Earnest appeal (4)
9 Sudden fear (5)
10 Herb related to parsley (7)
11 Amorously (12)
13 Outcome (6)
14 Small arboreal ape (6)
17 Imprudence (12)
20 Former (3-4)
21 Widespread dislike (5)
22 Disposed of for money (4)
23 Vision (8)

Down

1 Bites at (4)
2 Detection devices (7)
3 Absolute authority in any sphere (12)
4 Make empty (6)
6 Floor of a building (5)
7 Lessening (8)
8 Detailed reports (12)
12 Shining (8)
15 Kicking (7)
16 Avaricious (6)
18 Reside (5)
19 Leave out (4)

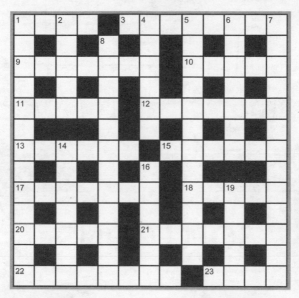

Across

1 Curl one's hair (4)
3 Highly productive (8)
9 Expressed indirectly (7)
10 Haggard (5)
11 Valuable thing (5)
12 Aquatic creature with prominent barbels (7)
13 Growing weary (6)
15 Symbol or representation (6)
17 Italian rice dish (7)
18 Levies; chimes (5)
20 Money container (5)
21 Tropical disease (7)
22 Where tents are pitched (8)
23 Country bordered by Libya and Sudan (4)

Down

1 Benevolent and generous (13)
2 Strong cords (5)
4 Lower (6)
5 Lawfully (12)
6 Pertaining to a river (7)
7 Reach the required standard (3,3,7)
8 Clarity (12)
14 Platform (7)
16 Way something is set out (6)
19 Deciduous coniferous tree (5)

SOLUTIONS

1

```
F  F  T     S  I  E  R  R  A
D  I  S  L  O  Y  A  L     A  M
E     A     P  U     F  I  B
D  R  A  G     I  T  S  E  L  F     L
   C     R     S  H        I     E
P  E  D  A  N  T  S     S  T  A  G  S
   N     S        B  A
L  A  S  T  S     B  A  S  K  E  T  S
O     W     D     N     E     A
G     A  S  K  I  N  G     O  U  R  S
J  O  Y     N     I     V     T
A     E     G  U  N  M  E  T  A  L
M  I  D  D  A  Y     G     R     N
```

2

```
B  A  L  L  C  O  C  K     S  C  A  M
O     O     A     O     U     O        I
U  N  C  U  T     O  M  N  I  B  U  S
I     U     E     L     B     R        C
L  A  S  E  R     E     E     A  S  H
L     T     P  E  R  I  L        I     E
A     S     I        I     U  N        V
B        L  O  O  S  E     N        I  V
A  P  T     L     F     V  I  D  E  O
I     A     A     F     A     E     U
S  A  M  U  R  A  I     B  I  R  D  S
E     S     S     S     L     G     L
E  N  D  S     T  H  R  E  N  O  D  Y
```

3

```
E  W  E  R     D  O  U  B  T  F  U  L
X     S     R     W     U     L        I
E  X  T  R  E  M  E     S  T  Y  L  E
M     E     M        I     L     S
P  E  R  F  O  R  M  A  N  C  E  S
L     R     A     E     A     T
A  R  C     S  I  N  K  S     F  A  R
R     H     E     I     S        E
   D  I  F  F  I  C  U  L  T  I  E  S
P     F     U        I     N     T
O  F  F  A  L     W  A  K  E  F  U  L
S     O     L     O     E     E     E
H  O  N  E  Y  B  E  E     A  R  E  S
```

4

```
P  A  S  S  P  O  R  T     O  P  U  S
O     U     R     O     D     A        I
L  U  N  G  E     M  O  I  S  T  E  N
E     B     S     A     S        I     I
   S  U  B  C  O  N  S  C  I  O  U  S
E     R     R     S     O        T
L  E  N  T  I  L     E  N  G  A  G  E
I     P     S     T     C     R
G  O  O  D  T  E  M  P  E  R  E  D
I     T     I     U     N     R     B
B  E  H  A  V  E  D     T  A  B  B  Y
L     E     E     G     I     E     E
E  U  R  O     H  E  A  D  A  C  H  E
```

5

```
A  N  T  E  C  E  D  E     S  W  A  M
L     H     L     U        I     A     I
A  O  R  T  A     G  E  N  E  R  A  L
S     I     I        C        E     K
   A  V  A  R  I  C  I  O  U  S  L  Y
O     E     V     O     R        W
B  U  D     O  W  N  E  R     L  E  A
L     Y     Y     E     I     A     Y
I  N  T  R  A  N  S  I  G  E  N  T
G     A     N        I     C     S
I  L  L  I  C  I  T     B  L  E  E  P
N     E     O     L     T     A
G  I  S  T     A  P  P  E  A  S  E  R
```

6

```
C  O  N  T  I  N  U  E     L  A  M  P
U     A     N     S        R        O
T  A  S  K  S     U  N  T  A  M  E  D
E     S     I     R        I        I
      A     S     P  O  L  E  N  T  A
E  Q  U  A  T  E  S     O     G     T
D     E        E     C        R        Y
U     S     N     A  N  A  R  C  H  Y
C  L  U  S  T  E  R     T     A
A     M        R        I     M     T
T  I  M  P  A  N  I     O  X  B  O  W
E     E        V     N     E     O
D  A  D  S     M  E  A  S  U  R  E  S
```

SOLUTIONS

7

```
L A U G H I N G G A S
E   R   I   G R   N E
X R   M E N S A   G U M
P R I S M   I   P E   A
E   V   I   T   H E R O N
C L E N C H E S     C
T   D   K       T S   I
A         D O O R S T O P
T I M E S   R   A A   A
I   O   L   G   C A R E T
O A T   A P A R T   L E
N   O   S   N       D
O R C H E S T R A T E
```

8

```
S T U M B L E S   L A M B
I   K   I   X   P P   R
C R U M B   O V E R A G E
K   L   L   D R   C   A
  D E L I Q U E S C E N T
S   L   O   S   E   H
P L E D G E   S V E L T E
A     R   S   E   O   D
C A N T A N K E R O U S
E   O   P   E   A D   W
M A T T H E W   N I E C E
A   E   Y   E   C   S   E
N O S Y   A R R E S T E D
```

9

```
  B A   M   D E A D E N
D O R M O U S E   R   U
L   B   M M   O W N   I
P E R U   B O O B O O   C
  R S   L   N   L   L I
C O C H L E A   G U S T O
  E   D   D   P
C H E S S   S I G H T L Y
A   L   T   V   E   I
N   D E C R E E   A R M Y
A G E   E   R   V   P
R   R   R   A N T E A T E R
D E S E R T   S L   T
```

10

```
M U S T   O B V I A T E D
E   I   S   U   N   O   A
R E F U T E D   S P R A T
I   T   R   G U R E
D I S S A T I S F I E D
I   I   E   F   N   N
A V E N G E   S E E T H E
N   T   H A   R       B
A   R E S T A U R A T E U R
R   R   A   R   B   L A
R E N E W   O B L I G E S
I   A   A   A   A K
A L L E Y W A Y   O R C A
```

11

```
B I R T H D A Y   G O B I
U E   I   I   X   N
S E N S E   R I N G L E T
I   E   R   I   V   E
N E W B O R N   U P P E R
E   A G G   L   E
S O L E L Y   U N T I E S
S   Y   S   E N T
W H O O P   T E R M I N I
O   G H   R   A T   N
M A R T I N I   B R I N G
A   E   C F   L   A L
N O S E   R E D E P L O Y
```

12

```
S E T A S I D E   S P U R
U   R   H E   C I E
C H I N A   P R O R A T A
K   L   R U   N   N S
  C O M P E T I T I O N S
I   G S Y   E   E
G L Y P H S   I M P E L S
N   O   C   P M   S
  I N T R O D U C T I O N
T   H T   D U T   E
I C E B E R G   O M I T S
N   R R   E U V   P
G U M S   B L U S T E R Y
```

13

```
C H A R I S M A   T O E S
O   L   N   O   A   S   H
M O I S T   D E F A C T O
P   A   R   E   T   A   O
L A S S O   S   E   R A T
E   E   D E T E R   I
M   S   U   T   S   N
E   C L O T H   N   G
N I B   T   R   O B O E S
T   A   O   N   U   W   T
A L G E R I A   G A M M A
R   E   Y   T   H   E   R
Y O L K   L E T T I N G S
```

14

```
  M A T R I M O N I A L
S U E   I   E   I   E L S
H   T   V E N U S   G Y M
O Z O N E   I   T   A   A
R   C   R   O   S T E E L
T A U N T I N G   L   M
C   E   S     C   S   M
H     L I B R E T T I   I
A R S O N   N U   I     N
N   A   E   T   I D L E D
G E L   A R E A S   T   E
E   V   R   N   E   O   D
  C O N S I D E R I N G
```

15

```
C O M B   M A S S A G E D
O   O   C   S   T   R   U
N O T I O N S   R E E K S
S   E   L   A   A   M   K
I N T E L L I G I B L Y
S   A   L   G   I   P
T H U M B S   R H I N A L
S   P   O   C   T   A
  U S E R F R I E N D L Y
A   W   A   E   N   I   B
C H E S T   D E E P S E A
N   P   O   I   R   C   C
E N T I R E T Y   C O O K
```

16

```
S T A N D O F F   A C T S
P   E   I   I   C   A   A
L Y R I C   S H O W M A N
E   A   T   H   M   E   C
N E T L I K E   P I L O T
D   E   O   S   L   I
I O D I N E   M A G N U M
F   A   S   C   O   O
E R R O R   C R E W M A N
R   O   I   A   N   I
O P U L E N T   T A N G O
U   S   S   H   L   A   U
S P E D   R E C Y C L E S
```

17

```
I N G E S T E D   S H E D
N   R   E   U   A   A   O
K N E L L   R O C K I N G
S   E   F   O   C   T   G
  I N T E R P R E T I V E
P   E   M   E   L     D
U N R I P E   W E A S E L
N   L   A   R   Q   Y
C I R R O S T R A T U S
T   E   Y   O   T   E   S
U N C L E A N   I N L E T
A   A   D   A   O   C   I
L O P E   C L I N C H E R
```

18

```
I O N S   H E A D R E S T
M   O   C   I   I   A   R
P R O L O N G   S Y R I A
E   S   M   H   B   T   N
R Y E   P   T   E T H O S
C   L O Y A L   L   P
E   P   E   I   Y   A
P E   T A B L E   A   R
T H R E E   A   V   A R E
I   T   N   F   I   D   N
B R U T E   F O N D A N T
L   R   S   L   G   G   L
E M B O S S E D   D E W Y
```

SOLUTIONS

19

```
M I R R O R I M A G E
E   M O   E   I   L A
N   M A F F I X   U R N
G L O O M   E U E   T
I   R   I   R   P A S T E
N E A T N E S S       C C
E   L G       S U   E
      F A S T E N E D
R E A C H   C   R C E
I   U I U   A D O R N
N U N   R E M I T   V C
G     T E E   U E E
A S T R O N O M E R S
```

20

```
M O D E     F L A I L I N G
I   O H E N   D       A
L E N D I N G   F O I S T
E   O P A E O       E
P E R S P I C A C I T Y
O   O Y T       I G
S N A P P Y   P I N C E R
T   V O D O       R E
  C O N T R I B U T I O N
I   I A L S D       A
M A D A M   A L L O Y E D
P E U T Y L E     L E
S I D E S T E P   E L K S
```

21

```
  E F F E C T I V E L Y
S   I Q   O E   U P
K E N   U T T E R   C O
Y   E I T   M A K E R
S T R A P   E O   I T
C       W R A N G L E R
C R   P L     T Y   A
A G I T A T O R       I
P C W   R       B E A S T
E N T R Y   I A B   I
R U   E A S E S   B U S
S   R R   O I O T
  P E R S O N A L I T Y
```

22

```
E N T I C I N G   S T A R
X   H O I   F R E
T I E I N   B E L G I U M
R   R G B   U A O
A D M I R A L   O R D E R
O   A A E   R S
R E L A T E   L E S S E E
D   U T S U L
I M P E L   R E C Y C L E
N   L A A C S
A S E P T I C   N O U N S
R   A E T C M L
Y E T I   A S S E M B L Y
```

23

```
C A R A P A C E   V E T O
O   E A   I U R   V
N I G E R   C O N N O T E
S   I T A D D R
T E M P I   D   E T A
E   E   C H A I R   M
L   S U   S B M
L   L I C I T   O I
A L L   A A   A L O F T
T   A R M F K I
I M P U L S E   F O L I O
O E Y   R E E U
N U L L   M A N D A T E S
```

24

```
D E D U C I N G   C H E F
E   R O O   I   O E
F E I G N   T U N I S I A
O   F T A S T   T
R E T R E A T   T R A S H
E   E M E R   E
S C R A P E   N U M B E R
T   O B C R W
A U G U R   O U T C O M E
T E A R   I M I
I G N O R E D   O W I N G
O I   I Y E N N H
N E E D   C R E S C E N T
```

SOLUTIONS

25

```
C O S M O L O G I S T
B   R   A   O   L E   Q
R A G   Y U C C A   G U
O   A   O   A   C O M M A
T E N O R   T   I   E   R
H       R E T A I N E R
E   E   C   L   T   E
R E P L A C E S       L
H   I   U   F   D E B T S
O A T H S   F   I   R   O
O   A   T W E E T   A I M
D   X   I   C   C   W   E
E Y E C A T C H I N G
```

26

```
R I F T   M I S S H A P E
A   U   D   N   U   V   X
D A N G E R S   R O O S T
I   G   L   I   R   C   R
O R I B I   D I O R A M A
A       C   E   U   D   V
C R A V A T   A N G O R A
T   M   T   H   D       G
I M P I E T Y   I N D I A
V   H   S   P   N   R   A
I R O N S   H I G H E S T
T   R   E   E   S   A   L
Y E A R N I N G   E M M Y
```

27

```
F I S T   L I T E R A T I
O   P   D   N   S   N   N
L E A P I N G   T O X I C
L   R   S   E   R   I   R
O A K   A S   A N O D E
W   T   S A T I N   U   D
T   M   T   G   S   U   U
H   U   R I N S E   L   L
R A D I O   O M   M O O
O   D   U   T   E   U   U
U N I T S   I G N O R E S
G   E   L   O   T   A   L
H U R R Y I N G   C L O Y
```

28

```
I M P R O P E R   S T E P
N   L   U   B   T   R   R
E N A C T   B U R R I T O
X   Y   S   I   A   E   P
P I P I T   N   N   R H O
E   E   R A G E S   F   C
R   N   E   F   C   T
I       T A S T E   A
E E L   C   A   R O M E O
N   Y   H   L   A   E   N
C H I M E R A   B U R M A
E   N   D   M   L   A   T
D O G S   L I C E N S E E
```

29

```
C O S T   C A L A M A R I
O   I   F   B   R   B   N
M A T U R E S   T R Y S T
P   U   A   O   I   S   R
A S P   U R   S A M B A
N   I   D E B U T   A   N
I   E   U   I   L   S   I
O   M   L O G I C   I   I
N O B L E   O A   E G G
A   R   N   L   L   T   E
B L A S T   D O L P H I N
L   C   L   E   Y   I   C
E V E R Y O N E   A C R E
```

30

```
M A G I C I A N   T A L C
O   R   O   G   T   D   A
B R O O M   O A R S M A N
S   W   M   U   I   I   A
    I N V E S T I G A T O R
V   U   N   I   G       I
I M P I S H   R E M A K E
S   S   U   V   R   M   S
C L E A R S I G H T E D
E   A   A   R   A   R   U
R E G A T T A   P A I N T
A   L   E   G   P   C   A
L I E D   P O L Y M A T H
```

SOLUTIONS

31

RUBY SOMBRERO / CARTOON ITCHY / CONFIDENTIAL / ENDEAR GROTTO / INDIVIDUALLY / GLEAN ALLEGRO / RESOLVES TREK

32

ROTS EMBOLDEN / INTONED OCEAN / COMIC LEAFLET / RUEFUL COERCE / ADOPTED OILED / IDIOM GRIFFIN / NAMEDROP LYRE

33

INSISTED AGED / DROOP ITALICS / VICAR TAP / NEEDS / TOWER / ART OTTER / ICELAND PITON / YOKE ADORABLE

34

CONSEQUENCE / BREAD MEN / DATES / WISER / STRAIGHT / THANKYOU / ASTIR / FORGO / LOB MOTIF / DOWNTRODDEN

35

EARTHENWARE / YAK PETER / PAWED REGAL / ORDNANCE / HINDMOST / EIDER / TAPER / OUGHT AGO / UTILITARIAN

36

RIFF OVERSTEP / GUZZLER BINGE / TRY LARGO / EERIE / TOKYO / SCUBA BOA / EVOKE SLEIGHT / SWEETEST DEFY

37

```
D R E S S I N G   R H E A
I X E   I   E     N
V O C A L   P E N S I O N   O
E   E F   C   S       O
P R A I S E W O R T H Y   I
E   P   N T M       I
N I T   T R U M P   K I N
V   E   D   A   N   G
I M P E R F E C T I O N
A   R E   I   W     H
B L O S S O M   B R I N E
L   N T   A L   N   R
E W E S   A R P E G G I O
```

38

```
J U S T   F A R C I C A L
E E   A   C U A     A
A N G E L I C   M O L E S
L   U   L E   U   D S
O V E R I N D U L G E D
U     M E   O   R S
S W A M P S   U N P A C K
Y L O A     I     Y
  A S T R O N O M I C A L
S O T C   B   H   I
C I R C A   H O U S I N G
U A   N O   S   L H
T I N C T U R E   S L O T
```

39

```
I N D I C A T E   C O M A
N R O   I N   P   B
C L E A N   P R O V E R B
O S V   O N   R   R
M A S T I F F   F L A R E
P E V   F L   V
E A R W I G   S A F A R I
T   A   S M   M A
E X C E L   C O M P O S T
N L I   R A   U I
T R U S T E E   B I N G O
L N Y   E L   T N
Y O G A   I N V E R S E S
```

40

```
S U R E   C H E C K I N G
L I E   I O   C U
I N D E X E D   N E E D Y
P G T   S   C S
P R E C O G N I T I O N
I   R O   I L   I
N A P   T A R O T   D U D
G A   I   T U   O
  H Y P O T H E T I C A L
S M N   T A A
T H E T A   L O O K O U T
E N T   E N W R
M U T T E R E D   E N V Y
```

41

```
C R I T I C A L   S P U D
H M N   B B I   I
R A P I D   R E L I E F S
O E E A   A T T
N O T E P A D   B U Y E R
O U E E B   R
L O S I N G   T E M P T S
O   D A R   R S
G L I D E   Z A M B E Z I
I N N A   O M N
C H A N C E L   U S I N G
A N E E T E L
L E E K   F A T H E R L Y
```

42

```
N O R M   P R O P O S E D
O O A O   H I A
T O N I G H T   O F F E R
E D R   T T N
B O O G I E W O O G I E
O   C E G N S
O P T   U N D E R   G E T
K R L G A U
  B O T T L E O P E N E R
S W U   H O G
C L E A R   B R E A T H E
A L A A R C O
N E S T L I N G   S H I N
```

SOLUTIONS

43

```
R I D E   L A R G E S S E
E   O   V   N   R T   K
A I R P O R T   A B A S E
S   I   C H C   T   S
S A C R I L E G I O U S
U   F   M   O   E   T
R E D D E N   Q U A S A R
E   A   R   P   S S   I
  H Y P O C H O N D R I A
F   T   U   O   E   A N
L A I R S   B A S H I N G
O   M   L   I   S   N L
E V E R Y D A Y   T Y P E
```

44

```
A S T O U N D S   E D I T
R   I   N E E   E   R
C O C O A   T E X T I L E
H   K   S E C   S   A
I T E M S   S H   M R S
T   T   U L T R A   U R
E   S   M   N   R E
C   I C I N G   N   G
T U B   N   N   E V I C T
U   E   G T A   G   R
R E V O L V E   B A N J O
A   E   Y   N L   E V
L I L Y   A T T E N D E E
```

45

```
R U D E   S P E C I F I C
E   E   E A O   A   R
C H I E F L Y   U N I F Y
E   S   F O N   L   P
P I T   O F   T R U S T
T   R I   R I F L E   T
I   R T   R   E   O G
V   O   L I L A C   G R
E L O P E   E L   T E A
N   M S   P A   E   P
E D I T S   T R I U M P H
S   E   L O M   P   E
S P R A Y I N G   S O A R
```

46

```
I N C L U D E S   A P E D
R   H   N L I   E   E
A W A R D   K E N N E L S
N   I   E   T   V   I
  E N T R E P R E N E U R
O   E   W L R   R
C O D   R E A R M   D E N
C   I   Z   I   I   G
U N A T T R A C T I V E
P   D   I   T   I   G
A L M A N A C   E L D E R
N   I   G U N   E   I
T E X T   J E T T I S O N
```

47

```
M I S S O U R I   O P A L
E   T   T E A   L   E
A B A S H   P E N G U I N
N   M   E E T   M   I
A P P R O A C H A B L E
D   E   W L R   N
R A D I O S   P O E T I C
I   R   B P R   Y
N O N A L C O H O L I C
K   O   D N L   A
I C I C L E S   O S I E R
N   S   Y A G   A K
G R E W   B I C Y C L E S
```

48

```
M U S E   S O R C E R E R
E   I   M R O   A   A
C O R P O R A   U S U R P
H   E   T C N   C   T
A N N I H I L A T I O N
N   H   E E   E U   A
I N B O R N   C R I S I S
C   E   T   I   P   S
  S E C O N D T O N O N E
M   L   N L I   U   S
A X I N G   I G N I T E S
L   N   U N T   E   E
I C E B E R G S   A R M S
```

SOLUTIONS

49
```
L O C K   C A N B E R R A
A   A   A   C   E   O   U
C E R A M I C   S P U R T
K   G   A   E   P   T   O
A T O L L   P R E M I U M
D   I   G   T   C   N   A
A P P E A R   A T T E S T
I   R   M   D   A       I
S T O R A G E   C I V I C
I   G   T   D   L   I   A
C O R G I   U T E N S I L
A   A   O   C   D   T   L
L A M I N A T E   H A Z Y
```

50
```
C O R E   O B S I D I A N
A   E   D   A   M   N   O
P E T R I F Y   P A S S E
A   R   S       R   I   L
C L O T H E S H O R S E
I     E   C   V   T   A
T U T   A B O D E   S O B
Y   H   R   U   M       U
  W E L T E R W E I G H T
P   O   E       N   U   M
A P R O N   O U T L I N E
I   E   E   R   S   D   N
R E M E D I E S   L E N T
```

51
```
  S I T T I N G D U C K
A N   O   E   U   O   P
C   Q   A S T E R   O D E
C H U M S   T   U   E   R
O   E   T   E   M O D E M
M I S D E E D S       A
P   T   R   F   M   N
A       O B D U R A T E
N E W L Y   I   C   R   N
I   O   O   K   H O I S T
E L M   K N I T S   T   L
D   E   E   N   I   A   Y
  I N E S T I M A B L E
```

52
```
B U D S   B A L A N C E D
R   A   H   V   L   A   E
A R T D E C O   P O P U P
I   U   A   U   H   E   E
N A M E D   C H A G R I N
S       M   H   N   E   D
T R A G I C   T U N D R A
O   B   S   R   M       B
R O S E T T E   E N N U I
M   T   R   S   R   I   L
I R A T E   C H I A N T I
N   I   S   U   C   T   T
G A N G S T E R   W H E Y
```

53
```
  A S S O C I A T I O N
D   P   V   N   O   S   M
E K E   A C H E D   S   A
R   A   T   E   D R I L L
M E R G E R   L   C   E
A       R E B E L L E D
T   A   B   R   E   I
O B S E R V E D       C
L   C   I   X   M E A N T
O V E R T   P   A   V   I
G   N   T R O L L   A D O
Y   T   L   R   T   I   N
  E S S E N T I A L L Y
```

54
```
T R E S P A S S   S H O O
A   V   R   O   D   A   N
C H I N O   P R E D I C T
T   D   P       L   K   H
  R E C O N S T I T U T E
A   N   R   C   B       D
N U T   T E R S E   T W O
E       I   E   R   I   T
C O M M O N W E A L T H
D   O   N       T   U   O
O R D E A L S   I D L E S
T   E   L   I   O   A   L
E L L S   S C E N A R I O
```

SOLUTIONS

55

```
D R A B   B A G U E T T E
I   M Q   K   N E   A
S T I M U L I   D A M E S
C   G   E   M E   P   Y
R O O M S   B A R B E L L
E       T   O   A   R I
D E V O I D   S C R A P S
I   E   O E   H     T
T E N A N T S   I S S U E
A   T A   P E   T     N
B L U R B   R A V I O L I
L   R   L I   E   M   N
E L E M E N T S   G A N G
```

56

```
A W A Y   S O U R N E S S
C   G H   V   E   L   I
C O L L E G E   A R I E L
O   O   A   R P   T   V
M E W   D D   P O I S E
P   A   Q U O T E   S   R
A C U     A   M   J
N O   A L D E R     U
I N N E R   I   A   D U B
M   Q   T A   N E   I
E L U D E   D E C I B E L
N   E   R E   E   A   E
T I R E S O M E   E R N E
```

57

```
F O O D   A L L E L U I A
O   C F   O   N   R L
R E T R A I N   C L A S P
G   E   I D   H   N H
E A T E N   O C A R I N A
T     T   N   N U   A
F I L T H Y   S T A M E N
U   U E   H I     D
L A M B A D A   N A C H O
N   B R   I   G R M
E X A C T   R E L E A S E
S   G E   D   Y W   G
S N O W D R O P   U L N A
```

58

```
C O D E   C L I N I C A L
O   E B   A   I O   E
L O P P I N G   G E N R E
L   O   O   H   T   R
A N T I C I P A T I O N
P   H U   C   R S
S O N   E X P E L   T A U
E   A   M A O     B
  A M B I D E X T R O U S
P   I S   H   L   I
O R B I T   Y I E L D E D
M   I R   O   S   E E
P L A T Y P U S   P R O D
```

59

```
D O M I N I O N   S C A B
A   A U   H   I A   L
D E C O R   M E M E N T O
O   H S   P O S     S
  N E V E R T H E L E S S
V   T   R   U   R   O
I C E   Y E T I S   V I M
S   R   O O   A     S
I N C O H E R E N T L Y
T   A Y   A   I I
O P T I M U M   T R A W L
R   E E   A   O N   L
S I R E   O P E R A T E S
```

60

```
S A M E   R E D F A C E D
T   I   Y   R A   A
I M M E N S E   O D D L Y
L   I S   N   E S   S
E X C R U C I A T I N G
T   F   D I   Z   P
T O O   F R E E S   A I R
O   P   I A   P     E
  T H I C K S K I N N E D
S   E I   E   A A
P U L S E   C Y C L I S T
A   I N A   E V   O
T R A C T O R S   T E A R
```

SOLUTIONS

61

```
C A K E   S C I M I T A R
O   A   B H O   A     O
N U R T U R E   U N D I D
T   M   R E   N     P   S
  E X A G G E R A T I O N
M     L       Y   A     E
P L A N A R   G I V E U P
T   E   R   I   N       I
  B R O A D C A S T I N G
P   O   L     I   N     R
L I B R A   C E D I L L A
O   I   R   L   E   A   P
D E C E M B E R   M Y T H
```

62

```
M E D I E V A L   W A S H
A   E   C   N   D L   Y
L E A S H   O V E R L A P
A   C   O   I   M O   E
D R O L L   N   O   W A R
M   N   O F T E N     C
I   S S   C     B R     I
N   I   A D O P T   A   R
I L L   T   T   R E B U T
S   E   I   A   Y   Y   I
T R E M O L O   B A S I C
E   R   N   S L   I   I A
R U S T   P E D E S T A L
```

63

```
W E P T   U M B R E L L A
O   A   B I E   A   G
R E L O A D S   P O W E R
D   E   N F E   S   E
P E R   T I   R O U T E
R     A T T I C   I   A
O S M     M   U T   B
C   Q   W A L L S   L
E X U D E   O   S   F E E
S   A   I   U I L
S H R U G   V I O L A T E
O   E   H   R   N   I   S
R O S E T T E S   A R T S
```

64

```
P R E C I N C T   J A V A
O   X   R   H C N G
P R I O R   I L L E G A L
E   G   E   O   L   I
R E A S S E S S M E N T
S   N   I L   E       T
Y E T   S T A F F   P I E
C       C   T   I E R
A R C H I T E C T U R E
M   A   B     T U E
O U T F L O W   I N S E T
R   C   E   O N   A   N
E C H O   M O N G O L I A
```

65

```
  A U D I O V I S U A L
B   N   S   E H C   A
A C   L I N G O   H O G
B A L S A   E   W E G
Y   E   N E   N A S A L
S T A N D A R D       O
I   R   S   F T   M
T     A P E R T U R E
T O T A L   E A   R   R
I   I A   P   Z E B R A
N E T   T O P A Z   I   T
G   A C E   L   N   E
  U N C H A R T E R E D
```

66

```
R I S K   S H R U G O F F
A   O   C   N   U   O
P A N T H E R   A F T E R
I   I   A   O N   P   D
D E C O M M I S S I O N
I   P   C   W S   P
T O R R I D   M E T T L E
Y   H   O   U   R   N
  D I N N E R J A C K E T
P   Z S   C   B   R   A
E P O C H   H U L K I N G
N   M   I I E   L   O
S W E E P I N G   E L A N
```

SOLUTIONS

67

I	N	S	E	C	U	R	E		O	V	E	R
I	N		C	O		I	D		O	E
T	H	R	U	M		D	R	E	A	D	E	D
O		U		P			C	K	D
A	F	F	E	C	T	I	O	N	A	T	E
C		F		N	O		N
L	A	Y		S	P	R	I	G		F	O	E
E			A		S	E	R	D
R	E	L	A	T	I	O	N	S	H	I	P
I		O	I			T	G	A
C	O	U	L	O	M	B		A	L	A	R	M
A	S		N		N	T	E
L	I	E	N		S	O	U	T	H	E	R	N

68

I	N	C	O	M	I	N	G		F	O	L	D
D		E		I	E		B	M	I
L	I	N	E	N		I	C	I	N	E	S	S
E		T	D	G	O	G	P
C	A	R	B	O	H	Y	D	R	A	T	E
A	U	O	S		I		N
G	A	R	A	G	E		E	V	A	D	E	S
I		G	S	E		E	E
T	O	T	A	L	I	T	A	R	I	A	N
A	I	I		R	S	N	S
T	O	R	O	N	T	O		I	D	E	A	L
E	E	G	B	T	R	I
D	O	D	O		D	E	W	Y	E	Y	E	D

69

P	E	A	K		R	E	D	H	E	A	D	S
E		L	U		N	O	W	O
R	I	P	E	N	E	D		M	I	N	I	M
S		H	I		E	I	E
P	L	A	I	N	S	A	I	L	I	N	G
I			T	W	E	G	T
R	U	B		E	X	A	M	S		S	E	W
E		U	R		I	S		E
I	M	P	E	R	T	I	N	E	N	C	E
A	P	S		E	A	T
J	O	I	S	T		H	O	S	T	I	L	E
A	N	E		I	S	L	R
R	I	G	I	D	I	T	Y		A	S	K	S

70

H	U	S	B	A	N	D	S		C	H	I	C
A		P	B	R	S		E	R
R	E	A	D	S		E	N	H	A	N	C	E
D	T	T	A	A	C	O
S	U	P	E	R	M	A	R	K	E	T	S
L	L	M	S	P		O
I	T	A	L	I	C		S	T	R	E	E	T
F		O	S	O	R		E
E	V	O	L	U	T	I	O	N	A	R	Y
S	B	S	S	E	G	A	A
P	R	E	P	L	A	N		U	N	T	I	L
A	Y	Y	N	E	U	U
N	E	S	T		C	A	R	D	A	M	O	M

71

T	U	R	N	C	O	A	T		I	D	E	A
A	O	O	C	S		I	P
C	A	B	I	N		T	W	O	S	T	E	P
K	B	T		M	T	O
D	I	S	I	N	G	E	N	U	O	U	S
S	N	N	R	A		I
L	U	G		U	N	A	R	M		C	U	T
I		O	S	B	O	E
P	R	E	S	U	M	P	T	U	O	U	S
P	A	S		L	R	H
E	N	G	U	L	F	S		I	C	I	L	Y
R		E	Y	I	S	E	M
Y	A	R	N		T	R	I	M	A	R	A	N

72

D		B		C		I	N	F	A	N	T
C	O	M	E	D	I	A	N		T		A
S		R		N	U		H	E	R
T	A	X	I		D	E	R	I	V	E		I
G		B	E	E		N	F
M	E	T	E	O	R	S		S	C	A	R	F
R	S	E	A
B	O	W	I	E		O	V	E	R	A	C	T
R		I	B	O	T	O
E		D	E	B	U	N	K		O	R	A	L
A	Y	E		F	I	O	R
D		S		F	O	N	D	N	E	S	S
S	I	T	U	P	S		G	S	E

73

```
M E D I A T O R   A P E S
A   I   V   U   U R U
G U A V A   T I N K E R S
E   L   I     P   E P
  B E L L I G E R E N C E
S   C   A   R O   C
P A T   B R I E F   B A T
U     I   M   I R   S
R E C O L L E C T I O N
I   U   I   A   W V
O R B I T E R   B A S T E
U   E   Y   A L E   I
S U D S   I N T E G R A L
```

74

```
S T A I R W A Y   A C I D
T   I   E   M S U   E
E A R T H   E P I G R A M
R   D   A   N N I   O
E N R O B E D   G R A I N S
O   O   I   S L
T O P P L E   W E I G H T
Y     I   R M O   R
P O S I T   A R I Z O N A
I   L   A   S N D   T
C R Y P T I C   D U B A I
A   L   E   A E Y   O
L A Y S   B L U D G E O N
```

75

```
E B B S   R E A B S O R B
N   E   I   M A R   R
C L E A N U P   C A I R O
O   C   F L T   G   K
U S H E R   O V E R A W E
R   I   Y   R M   N
A L I E N S   F I N I S H
G   R   G S O     E
E M I N E N T   L E M M A
M   D   M   A O   R
E L I D E   N E G L E C T
N   U   N C Y   T E
T O M A T O E S   U S E D
```

76

```
C O L L I E R Y   Z I N C
H   O   N   E A T   H
R O B O T   S O P R A N O
Y   S   E I P   L   R
S E T T L E S   R H Y M E
A   E   L T E   O
N O R D I C   S H Y I N G
T     G   I E R
H O R S E   G O N D O L A
E   E   N N S N   P
M O R O C C O   I R I S H
U   U   E   R O N   E
M I N D   T E E N A G E R
```

77

```
E A S T   E T H I O P I A
S   U   I   N E V
C L E A N E R   T I T L E
A   D   C A E   U   R
P R E P O N D E R A N T
A   N   E C I   L
D E S I S T   N E V A D A
E   H   I G P   G
  E A R S P L I T T I N G
E   M   T O I   G A
L A P S E   B R O I L E R
M   O   N E N   O D
S H O R T E S T   T O P S
```

78

```
R E E F   A R A C H N I D
E   G   I U   H O   E
C O R O N E T   R A T E S
H   E   C   I   K
A S T R O P H Y S I C S
R   N   I   T E E
G A P   V E N O M   S I X
E   L   E G A   C
Q U I N T E S S E N C E
L   N   I   E A S
A N D R E   D E V I C E S
S   N   O   E R E
H E R I T A G E   B E T S
```

SOLUTIONS

79

```
E S P E C I A L   D A F T
S   A   P   C   L   E
T H R O B   P E R F O R M
A   S   I   E   O   H   P
B O N A N Z A   S T A V E
L   I   E   L   S   R
I N P U T S   Z E U G M A
S   M   S   X   I   M
H Y E N A   W R A N G L E
M   N   K   A   M   G   N
E N T R E A T   I S L E T
N   E   R   H   N   E   A
T E R M   R E V E R S A L
```

80

```
R U G S   D I S S E C T S
A   R   C   M   I   O   I
C L E A R U P   M I N E D
C   B   O   I   E
O V E R S I M P L I F Y   Y
O   S   E   A   E   P
N U B   C O D E R   R U E
S   R   O   I   I   N
  M A N U F A C T U R E D
B   G   N   I   E   U
L I G H T   F R E T F U L
O   E   R   I   S   E   U
W O R R Y I N G   D R U M
```

81

```
S T R E A M   B   A   S
A   U   U N E N D I N G
L E D   S   T   V   E
L   D I T H E R   O V E N
O   E   Y   A   C   R
W O R D Y   S Y N A P S E
E   P   S   T
B R A V E R Y   B E L O W
E   E   E   A   O   E
E V I L   F A B R I C   A
E   E   O   A   H   A M P
G A Z P A C H O   L   O
L   S   E   R E A S O N
```

82

```
H E C T A R E S   I R O N
I   A   C   A   B   E   A
G I R T H   S E R P E N T
H   R   I   A   V   I
A T O N E   N   I   E G O
N   T   V E G A N   O   A
D   S   E   W   N   L
M   M O C H A   I   N
I R E   E   O   S U S H I
G   L   N   R   H   I
H A B I T A T   I N G O T
T   O   S   E   N   H   I
Y E W S   E X E G E T I C
```

83

```
O V A L   T A J M A H A L
V   M   A   N   U   A   U
E M B A S S Y   L O G O S
R   I   T   H   T   G   T
P A T H O L O G I C A L
A   N   W   L   R   D
S P I R I T   B I R D I E
S   D   S   C   N   C
M Y T H O L O G I C A L
E   L   M   O   U   A   A
D E L V E   S C A R P E R
G   I   N   E   L   E   E
E T C E T E R A   A R I D
```

84

```
P A G E   B L A C K O U T
O   A   S   O   A   U   O
S O M E H O W   R A T T Y
S   U   O   D   G   S
I N T E R M E D I A R Y
B   T   R   O   O   F
L A B   C R U E L   W H O
E   E   H   P   O   R
  A D V A N T A G E O U S
B   R   N   I   V   A
A L O N G   C A S S O C K
T   O   E   O   T   I   E
H U M I D I T Y   E D E N
```

85

```
A R C S   V O L C A N I C
R   A   B   C   I   U   O
G E N E R I C   R I P E N
U   O   E   U   R   T   S
M A N N A   P R O V I S O
E   S   Y   C   A   L
N I C E T Y   N U C L E I
T   O   S   W   M   D
A M M E T E R   U M B R A
T   P   R   I   L   T
I M A G O   T S U N A M I
V   C   K   H   S   D   O
E S T E E M E D   T E E N
```

86

```
W I N D P I P E   T H U D
A   U   A   O   B   A   E
R A R E R   S T R A N D S
Y   S   O   E   E   O   I
  D I S C O U R A G I N G
P   N   H   R   T   N
R E G A I N   T H R I C E
O   A   O   T   N   D
D O U B L E D E A L E R
U   S   I   E   K   X   S
C L A U S E S   I D A H O
E   G   M   S   N   C   U
R E E L   D A U G H T E R
```

87

```
  D E T E R M I N I S M
T   N   R   A   O   A   I
E D   O N S E T   F A N
R I L E D   C   E   E   T
M   E   I   O   D I R G E
I N S A N I T Y   L   L
N   S   G   A P L
    C O N C E R T I
L E F T S   B   O   A G
O   A   I   O   L A T H E
G N U   D A I S Y   T   N
Y   N   L   S   T L T
  P A R E N T H E S E S
```

88

```
A C C E S S   P   V   B
C   L   W A R R I O R S
E R A   I   U   R   O
T   M U F F I N   T A N S
I   M   I   U   Z
C R Y P T   E N D O W E D
U   P   G   S
K R Y P T O N   W I N C H
E   P   A   F   E
C L U E   C A L L U P   L
I   T   H   O   H I P
O V E R H E A R   E   E
E   Y   R   A N S W E R
```

89

```
I N C H   D I L I G E N T
R   A   D   N   X   H
R U N N E R S   T H E R E
E   N   L   T   E   R   O
S A Y   I E   R O T O R
P   O   G A P E S   E   E
O   R   H   E   D   T
N   U   T U N I C   I
S T I F F   U   T   T I C
I   N   U   R   I   A   A
B R O I L   S N O R K E L
L   U   L   E   N   E   L
E S S A Y I S T   P R E Y
```

90

```
  P R O G R E S S I V E
O   E   R   N   T   A   I
M D   A U D I O   G E M
N O W I N   I   I   U   P
I   O   T   N   C H E E R
S T O N E A G E   E   S
C   D   D   W   F
I   C R E A T O R S
E R A S E   E   R   U   I
N   N   D   A   M A N G O
C A N   U N D U E   D   N
E   O   C E S E   S   S
T Y P E W R I T E R S
```

SOLUTIONS

91

```
R E M A I N E D   D A M P
A   E   N   X       U   E
Y O L K S   T R A M P E D
S   O   O   A   A   A
    D   M   N E E D I N G
B A Y O N E T   Y   R O G
R   I   E
E   P   A   S H O R T L Y
A P R I C O T   P   E
K   I   A   E   N   F
I N S P E C T   N A D I R
N   O   E   E   O   E
G E N E   E S T R A N G E
```

92

```
B O W S   M U S C U L A R
E   A   P   N   O   E   O
D E S I R E S   N E X U S
L   T   E   U   S   I   Y
I N E X P E R I E N C E
N     O   E   R   O   R
E M B O S S   A V E N U E
N   R   T   N   A       P
  L I F E S E N T E N C E
T   S   R   U   I   A   A
O U T D O   R E V I V A L
F   L   U   A   E   E   E
U T E N S I L S   G L A D
```

93

```
  T O U R D E F O R C E
A   V   U   N   A   I   L
P E S I T E S   D U E   V
H O R N S   A   I   E   V
R   S   I   I   S E R V E
O P E R A B L E       L
D   E   N   R   J   H
I       A B N E G A T E
S E W E D   R   F   C   A
  E   U   E   R O U N D
A W E   O B E S E   Z   D
C   P   M   Z   S   Z   D
  P Y R O T E C H N I C
```

94

```
D I S H   A C I D R A I N
I   H   R   A   O   D   I
S U R V E Y S   M E D I C
P   U   F   U   E   E   K
E M B A R R A S S I N G
R     I   L   T   D   F
S H A G G Y   V I V A C E
E   D   E   S   C     A
  C H I R O P R A C T O R
O   E   A   L   L   Y   L
B U R S T   E L L I P S E
O   E   O   E   Y   E   S
E N S H R I N E   O D D S
```

95

```
D I D A C T I C   K I W I
O   R   R   M   C   N   N
U S U R Y   P R O S A I C
B   M   P   O   I   P   O
L I M I T   R   N   T O R
E   E   O P T I C   R   R
J   R   G   I   A   U
O     R A T E D   V   P
I V Y   A   O   E V E R T
N   E   P   M   N   N   I
T R A C H E A   T H U M B
E   S   Y   T   A   E   L
D A T A   C O A L E S C E
```

96

```
G U T T U R A L   A M I D
U   R   N   P   C   U   I
S T A I R   A T L A S E S
H   P   E   T   O   I   C
  M E T A P H Y S I C A L
C   Z   S   Y   E     O
O R E G O N   E M B E R S
N     N   G   O   N   E
C O U R A G E O U S L Y
E   P   B   N   T   I   G
R E S O L V E   H O V E R
T   E   R   E   E   I
O U T S   P A R D O N E D
```

97

```
Q U A G M I R E   C H U M
U   S U   U   C A   E
E A S E L   G R O W L E D
S   A   T   G N   L   I
T A U R I N E   V I S I T
I   L   L   D A     E
O U T L A Y   G L I D E R
N   T   S   E E   R
N E R V E   C A S S A V A
A   E   R Y   C D   N
I N S T A N T   E N S U E
R   T   L   H N E   A
E L S E   R E S T R A I N
```

98

```
H O G S H E A D   A S I A
E   R A C   D Q   C
A L I B I   A Z I M U T H
P   N   R C S   I   I
I N A D M I S S I B L E
P   E   R A   E   V
L O D G E R   T R I P L E
O   S   T   T R D
D O M E S T I C A T E D
D   Y I S   T C S
I N T E N T S   I N E P T
N   H G   U O D   U
G A S P   S E I N F E L D
```

99

```
S Y M P A T H Y   I C E S
O   E   L I   C O   H
B E R Y L   S C O R P I O
S   M I   N   R R
M A T T E R O F F A C T
A   I E   E O   A
B I D   R U L E R   G I G
S   A   I M A   E
U N D E T E C T A B L E
R   R   I   T I O
D R A G O N S   I N L A W
L   W N   K O E   E
Y A L E   L I G N E O U S
```

100

```
A T T A C H E D   F I R M
U   O   O R N   N I
R O B I N   R E A D E R S
A   A T   A R R   T
S C R E E N W R I T E R
A   C M   T O U
D R O O P S   S W O O P S
A   T   L M C   T
P A R S I M O N I O U S
T   E B U N   L A
I N S U L I N   D E I G N
N   E E G   E S N
G E T S   V E N D E T T A
```

101

```
  D I S H O N E S T L Y
R   S I E   H A C
U O   S O L V E   D U O
L U T E S   S   E   N
E O   O   R U N I N   O
O P P O N E N T     O
F   E G   S   E I
T     D I P L O M A S
H I D E S   S O B S
U E   C R   W E A V E
M O B   A M A Z E   R U
B   I L E   S G R
S T I P U L A T I O N
```

102

```
C R E E P I N G   G L U E
O   N R O   A O   M
N I C H E   D I S T U R B
S   L D D T   S E
P R O T E G E   R O Y A L
I   S C D   O L
C H E W E D   A L K A L I
U   S E O   B S
O G L E S   R O G U I S H
U U O R   I D M
S A N G R I A   C R I M E
L   A S T   A N N
Y A R D   F A N L I G H T
```

SOLUTIONS

103

```
A L A R M I S T . E M I T .
C . M . A . E . A . I . R
H E A T S . V E R A N D A
Y . T . S . E . I . O . N
. T E M P E R A T U R E S
. H . U . R . E . H . . F
H E N R O O T . I M P E D E
. D . T . E . N . N . . R
O B S C U R A N T I S M .
I . A . C . U . I . I . O
N E S T E G G . C A G E D
E . S . D . H . A . N . E
S A Y S . S T Y L I S T S
```

104

```
C A U L D R O N . J U D O
O . N . I . P . C . N . V E
M U S E S . E V A S I V E
B . O . R . R . T . T . R
A M U S E . R A . . Y E S
T . N . P E S T S . T . A T
I . I . D . U . . T . M I .
V . . . U . T U B E R . I T
E L F . A . A . . O U N C E
N . I . B . N . P . E . M
E P S I L O N . H O R D E
S . T . E . E . . I . . A N
S A S H . B R A C E L E T
```

105

```
. B . S . O . C L O S E D
S L O T H F U L . . P . E
E . A . F . I . . O A F .
C A L M . S E C T O R . I N
. T . P . E . K . T . . N
A S P E C T S . T H Y M E
. . . D . S . D . A . .
A D D E R . R E D R A F T
R . E . . B . G . A . O
E . P I L L A R . N U N S
N I L . . O . E . G . D .
A . O . W O E F U L L Y .
S T Y L E S . S . E . Y
```

106

```
C H O O S I N G . H A L F
O . U . T . A . P . G . I
W A T E R . B A H R A I N
S . C . A . I . P . I . I
. F R U I T F U L N E S S
F . O . U . H . . . H . H
L I P . H Y D R A . G E E
Y . . T . G . . U . S .
P R E D E T E R M I N E .
A . L . N . . O . B . U
P L A C E B O . N O O K S
E . N . D . D . I . A . E
R E D S . E D U C A T E S
```

107

```
. P A S S T H E B U C K .
M . R . O . A . A . U . E
E R R . B O W E D . M . L
A . O . E . A . D O U S E
N E W E R . I . E . L . P
I . N . . A I R B R U S H
N . S . S . . T . S . A .
G R U M P I L Y . . . N .
L . B . A . A . B L O A T
E X U L T . P A P . I .
S . N . T A P E S . I O N
S . I . E . E . E . N . E
. S T A R S T U D D E D
```

108

```
Q U A Y . P E R F U M E S
U . R . C . R . O . I . P
I S O L A T E . R A T I O
C . M . R . C . M . O . N
K N A V E . T R A N S I T
T . . L . S . L . I . . A
E X C E E D . O D D S O N
M . H . S . A . E . . . E
P L E A S E D . H E L L O
E . R . N . M . Y . O . U
R O U G E . I N D U C E S
E . B . S . R . E . A . L
D I S A S T E R . P L A Y
```

109

```
  A D V E N T U R O U S
T   I   L   A U   R   M
R I S   I D L E R   B Y E
I N D E X   E   A   A   A
C   A   I   N   L U N G S
E M I G R A T E       U   R
R   N   S     P   B     U
A     E S C A L A T E     M
T E R M S   I   R   C     M
O   E   T   L   A N K L E
P I P   O V E N S   I     N
S   E   R   N   O N   T
  C L I M A T O L O G Y
```

110

```
E N T H A L P Y   A P S E
R   R G   A   H A     M
G O I N G   R O O F T O P
O   S   R   P   H T     T
    R E L E N T L E S S L Y
A   C   S   H   L       I
C A T   S I E G E   F U N
C   I   I   I   S E G
I M P O V E R I S H E D
D   L   E     N   D   W
E N A B L E D   E L I T E
N   T   Y   O S   N   D
T I E S   M E S S A G E S
```

111

```
A R C H   S I M U L A T E
N   A D R   N   R F   V
T O R P E D O   S U R G E R
I   O   M N I     E I     R
C O L   O   N   A N V I L
L     N E C K S   O   L
I   V   S     O O L
M   I   T A K E N
A M B E R   I   A   P H I
C   R A   T   B B R     N
T R A I T   T I L T I N G
I   T   E     E E   D   L
C L O U D I N G   V E R Y
```

112

```
R A N K   E F F L U E N T
E   E   F   A   O Y   I
D A P P L E D   S T E E R
U   A Y   T   L   E
C A L L I G R A P H E R
I   I   N   A   R T   U
N O W   G E C K O   S I P
G   R   S   E   P   S
  D I S A G R E E M E N T
E G   U     G   R A   R
M A G I C   A R T I S T E
U   L   E   C   Y   E   A
S H E R R I E S   A D A M
```

113

```
A R T Y   S K I P P I N G
P   W D   E   Y   N   O
P R A I R I E   R O D E O
R   N   E   P   O   E   D
E R G   S   E   T O X I N
H   E     S P R E E   A
E   P   I     C   S T   U
N   E   N Y M P H       U
S L A N G   A   N   F I R
I   S   D   L   I U     E
B R A V O   I N C I T E D
L   N   W   C   S   O   L
E X T E N D E D   O N L Y
```

114

```
H U S H   F A N C I F U L
A   E   R   I   O O     I
R E D H E A D   U R G E D
D   A Q     R   H   S
C O N S U L T A T I O N
O   O   I   I   M   R   S
P E W   R U M B A   N O T
Y   A E   I   R       A
  P R E M E D I T A T E D
C   L   E     I   H     I
A C O R N   P L A T E A U
L   Č   T     A   M   M
L A K E S I D E   S E E S
```

SOLUTIONS

115

```
I N S C R I B E   A T O M
M   C   U   E   D   O   I
P R A W N   F R I E N D S
R   P   O   O   S   I   M
A Q U I F E R   A C C R A
C   L   T   E   F       N
T R A S H Y   A F R I C A
I       E   G   E   M   G
C H A R M   A S C R I B E
A   G   I   T   T   T   M
B R A I L L E   I M A G E
L   T   L   A   O   T   N
E V E N   F U N N I E S T
```

116

```
D R E A R Y   S   A   U
E   U     I M P O S I N G
J A R   E   U   S   C
E   O C U L A R   E E L S
C   P     D   R   M   O
T R A C K   H E R B A G E
    O   T   D   L
S C A N D A L   S E T U P
  L   V   M   S     R   L
M I N E   P A P A Y A   A
  C   N   E   E     M A Y
R H E T O R I C   P   E
E   S   S     S E N S O R
```

117

```
D E F I A N C E   A B U T
U   O   R   A   O   I   O
S O L A R   L I B E R I A
T   I   A   L   L   C   N
  M A L N O U R I S H E D
S   T   G   S   T       F
T I E R E D   L E D G E R
R   R   M   S   R   L   O
O V E R E M P H A S I S
E   N   N   I   T   M   S
G R E E T E D   I N P U T
L   M   S   E   O   S   E
Y O Y O   T R A N S E C T
```

118

```
F E B R U A R Y   B L O C
L   O   N   O   C   E   O
A I M E D   B R O A D E N
S   B   I   O   N   G   S
H E A D S E T   Q U E S T
I   S   C   S   U       R
N A T I O N   M I L I E U
T       V   T   S   M   C
H A L V E   H O T S P O T
E   A   R   A   A   I   I
P A R V E N U   D I N G O
A   V   D   S   O   G   N
N E A P   S T A R T E R S
```

119

```
R I B S   C R O S S B O W
E   E   C   O   T   O   E
D I S C O R D   R I T E S
G   E   S   A   A   T
I N T I M I D A T I N G
A     O   R   O   I   M
N E W   P L I E S   C O O
T   H   O   E   P       N
  K I L L E R W H A L E S
M   T   I     E   I   T
A V E R T   D U R A B L E
M   S   A   A   E   E   R
A U T O N O M Y   A L M S
```

120

```
A R T I F I C E   A F A R
I   Y     L   U   I   L E
D O P E Y   R E M A I N S
E   I   O     M   N   I
  A C K N O W L E D G E D I
C   A     T   R   A
O W L   H O O K S   M A N
N     E   T   U   E   G
S T R A W B E R R I E S
T   A   A     A   T   M
R U M B L E S   B R I B E
U   P   L   A   L   N   S
E A S E   S T R E N G T H
```

SOLUTIONS

121

```
I O T A   M A L D I V E S
N   H   M S   I   E   U
D A I S I E S   S T R O P
E   N   S   I   P   T E
T I G E R   S I L L I E R
E   E   T   A   G   F
R E C I P E   S C R O L L
M   L   R   P   E   U
I N A N E L Y   M O T T O
N   S   S   T E   R   U
A I S L E   H U N T E R S
C   I   N   O   T   A L
Y A C H T I N G   E D G Y
```

122

```
F O X Y   S P E C I M E N
E   Y   E O   O   A   O
R E L A X E D   N O R S E
O   E   T   S   I   S
C O M B I N A T I O N S
I   N   L   S   E   B
T I P   G R E E T   R I A
Y   E U R   E   E A   B
  I N D I S T I N C T L Y
C   N   S   T   O   H
H E A T H   C A L Y P S O
U   N   E   O Y   I   O
B A T H R O B E   I C E D
```

123

```
P I C T U R E S   A B E T
O   O   N N   P O   A
S T U F F   I N R O A D S
S   N   O   G   O S   T
I N C U R   M   F   T I E
B   I   G L A Z E   L
I   L   I   S   C E
L   V A S E S   R   S
I R K   A A   I D O L S
T   N   B W O   O   N
I D E A L L Y   N U D G E
E   L   E E   A E   S
S I T E   P R E L U D E S
```

124

```
A L S O   U N D E R C U T
L   H   D A   F   O   I
T E E M I N G   F I L E D
R   L   S   E   O   Y
U N F L A T T E R I N G
I   G   H   V   E   S
S E A   R E U S E   L I E
M   C   E   M S   V
  I R R E S P E C T I V E
S   O   A   L   E   R
K E B A B   B O N F I R E
I   A   L   E T   A   L
T A T T E R E D   I D L Y
```

125

```
L I C K   S C U D D I N G
E   A   S   L   E N   O
C O M P E R E   S E D G E
T   E   L   N   P U   S
U N O F F I C I A L L Y
R   L   H   I   G   D
E A R N E R   G R E E C E
R   O   S   F   I   C
  Q U E S T I O N M A R K
F   N   N N   G N   H
A D D L E   A T L A N T A
R   E   S   L Y   U   N
M O R A S S E S   F L E D
```

126

```
D R I V E W A Y   E V E R
O   N   N   N D   I   E
U N F I T   N A I R O B I
B   A   H U   S L   N
L I N G U A L   C H A F F
E   T   S   S O   O
C O S M I C   A N T L E R
R   A   O   S   E   C
O R C A S   P R O B A T E
S   A   T   T L   K   M
S A S H I M I   A B A T E
E   E   C   M T   G   N
R E D O   P A V E M E N T
```

SOLUTIONS

127

```
L E V Y   S C O O T E R S
O   I   S   L C   N   O
C O L L U D E   C O V E R
A   L   B   R   A   I   T
T R A N S M I S S I O N
I       T   C   I   U   F
N O R M A L   F O S S I L
G   A   N   V   N       U
  T I T T L E T A T T L E
B   D   I   R   L   E   N
A R E N A   B A L L A S T
L   R   T   A   Y   S   L
M A S T E R L Y   D E N Y
```

128

```
C O R N   A T L A N T I C
O   I   I   O   P   U   O
N O O D L E S   P O S E R
T   J   L   S   R   S   R
E V A D E   E Y E S O R E
N   G   S   C   C   C   S
T R I V I A   P I C K U P
E   G   T   S   A       O
D E N T I S T   T O K E N
N   M   R   I   O   D
E X T R A   O B V I A T E
S   E   T   L   E   L   N
S U D D E N L Y   D A R T
```

129

```
D E T A C H E D   F L A K
I   O   R   N   S   L   N
F O R C E   C H I C A G O
F   N   A   O   T   M   W
E X A C T E D   T R A I L
R   D   I   E   I       E
E V O L V E   I N D E E D
N       E   A   G   V   V
T A L O N   M E D I A T E
I   A   E   B   U   S   A
A B Y S S A L   C L I M B
T   E   S   E   K   O   L
E A R S   P R E S E N C E
```

130

```
  W H I T E C O L L A R
R   Q   A   O E S   A
E   M   F L U N G   H O B
S N I F F   R   A   E   B
T   N   E   T   L O S E R
A C I D T E S T   S   T V
U   D   A       S T R A M I
R       P A S T R A M I A
A L T O S   R   I   M   A
N   E   L   A   R E A C T
T O E   U M B E R   R   E
S   T   R   L   E   I D
  S H E P H E R D I N G
```

131

```
F A S T   C A T A L Y S T
I   C   D   S   D   E   O
E A R N E R S   D E A L T
N   U   C   E   I   R   S
D E B I L I T A T I N G
I       A   S   I   E   A
S E C U R E   W O O D E N
H   H   A   B   N       G
  P I T T E R P A T T E R
S   G   I   O   L   H   I
K E N D O   W E L C O M E
I   O   N   S   Y   R   S
P U N I S H E D   G N A T
```

132

```
C O L O P H O N   S H O E
I   I   R   D   P   E   X
R O G U E   I K E B A N A
C   H   S   O   N   P   G
U N T I E   U   U   S A G E
M       U   N O S E S   R
S   P   T   Y   P   R   A
T   A W F U L   L   L   A
A N T   T   L   V A U L T
N   A   I   U   A   M   E
C O M P O S E   N O M A D
E   E   N   I   E   L
S O S O   S T E A L T H Y
```

133

D	R	O	P		C	O	L	U	M	B	U	S
I		R		W			G		N		U		H
S	L	I	T	H	E	R		D	E	L	T	A
C		O		O		E		E		B		M
R	E	N	A	L		S	C	R	O	O	G	E
E			E		S		G		U		L
T	R	O	P	H	Y		H	A	S	S	L	E
I		V		B		R			L		S
O	R	E	G	A	N	O		M	A	K	E	S
N		R		R		W		E		I		N
A	U	D	I	T		M	O	N	O	C	L	E
R		U		E		A		T		K		S
Y	I	E	L	D	I	N	G		A	S	P	S

134

D	I	A	G	R	A	M	S		S	A	R	I
I		V		E		A		C		T		N
S	W	A	M	P		D	R	O	P	O	F	F
R		R		O		E		N		M		I
E	X	I	T	S		U		G		S	U	N
		C		S	E	P	A	L		I		T
P		E		E			O		A		T	E
E			S	C	R	A	M		N			E
C	U	B		S		E		E	D	G	E	S
T		U		I		G		R		R		I
F	U	R	L	O	N	G		A	X	I	O	M
U		N		N		A		T		E		A
L	A	T	H		D	E	F	E	R	R	A	L

135

T	R	A	N	S	A	C	T		R	A	M	S
O		S		T		A		D		P		U
S	U	P	E	R		R	A	I	N	I	N	G
S		H		O		A		S		A		G
	M	A	G	N	I	F	I	C	E	N	C	E
W		L		G		E		O			S
O	T	T	A	W	A		I	N	S	E	C	T
N		I		S		N		N		S
D	E	V	E	L	O	P	M	E	N	T	S
R		O		L		A		C		H		J
O	U	T	W	E	A	R		T	R	U	C	E
U		E		D		S		E		S		E
S	U	R	F		H	E	A	D	G	E	A	R

136

E	N	O	R	M	O	U	S		E	G	G	S
X		C		I		N		C		E		E
P	U	T	T	S		F	R	O	N	T	A	L
R		O		A		U		U		U		F
E	M	B	E	D		R		N		P	E	A
S		R		V	A	L	E	T			W
S		R		E			R		N		A	R
I		N	E	R	V	Y		E			R
O	U	R	T		T		E		W	H	E	R	E
N		U		U		A		O		D		N
I	M	P	E	R	I	L		M	E	L	E	E
S	E	E		L		A		E	S
M	I	E	N		H	Y	P	N	O	S	I	S

137

T	I	D	I	E	S		G	E	T
U		A		C	U	L	T	U	R	A	L
R	U	M		O		A		P		N
N		A	D	O	R	E	S		H	I	N	T
U		S		N		S	O		I
P	O	K	E	R		H	E	A	R	I	N	G
		N		H	S		I
S	T	A	G	G	E	R		M	A	M	B	A
	H		A	R	Y		I		D
T	W	I	G		E	X	A	C	T	S		A
A		I		T	C		C	O	G
B	R	A	N	D	I	S	H		U		E
	T		G		C		T	O	W	E	L	S

138

M	O	C	C	A	S	I	N		S	L	A	M
U		L		D		L		S	A		A
G	L	E	A	M		K	N	I	T	T	E	R
S		A		O			G		T		I
	T	R	A	N	S	C	E	N	D	E	N	T
D		E		I		H		I			I
E	A	R		S	P	O	O	F		M	U	M
M			H		I		I		I		E
A	L	L	E	M	B	R	A	C	I	N	G
N		E		E		A		U		A
D	I	V	I	N	E	R		N	A	T	A	L
E		E		T		I		C		E		P
D	I	R	E		O	B	S	E	S	S	E	S

SOLUTIONS

139

```
C U P O L A     D   T   F
R   L     B R I G H T E N
U S A   B   S   U   N
S   S C H E M A   M I N K
T   M   Y   V   B   E
Y E A R N   F O S S I L S
    A   D   W   U
H E A R E R S   A P P L E
  D   E   A   W   A   X
L I O N   P L A N E T   E
  T   E   E   L   R I M
B O W S P R I T   O   P
R   S   S   Z E A L O T
```

140

```
T R O P I C A L   S C A R
E   R   N   R   T   R   E
L E A S T   A T H E I S M
E   C   E   B   B   M   O
M O L A R   I   R   P U T
A   E   M A C R O   T   E
R   S   E       U   H   C
K     D E B U G   A   O
E W E   I   E   H U M A N
T   V   A   R   F   S   T
I N E R T I A   A C T O R
N   N   E   T   R   E   O
G A S H   C E R E B R A L
```

141

```
B A C K R E S T   T H U S
U   H   E   D   O   T
G R O O M   S H I A T S U
S   I   U   A   S   E   D
  E C O N O M I C A L L Y
P   E   E   E   R   L   Y
R O S A R Y   S U M M O N
E     A   B   R   A   G
C O N S T R U C T I N G
I   A   I   R   E   A   G
O B V I O U S   O C C U R
U   A   N   A   U   L   I
S I L K   P R O S P E C T
```

142

```
C A S E M E N T   S H O P
H   A   E   H   A     R
A B U Z Z   W R E S T L E
R   N   Z   E   N   E   T
A U T H O R S   C A D R E
C   E   S   T   E     N
T E R R O R   E F F O R T
E     P   U   O   R     I
R O V E R   P O R T I C O
L   I   A   R   W   F   U
E N T E N T E   A C I D S
S   A   O   A   R   C   L
S U L K   D R U D G E R Y
```

143

```
D Y N A M I S M   G A R B
O   O   U   A   U   P   A
E X T O L   C E N T R A L
R   I   T   R   A   I   L
  A C C I D E N T A L L Y
I   E   P   D   T     H
M E D A L S   C A L I C O
M   I   C   I   N   O
I N D O C T R I N A T E
N   R   I   A   A   E   W
E L E C T E D   B E N C H
N   S   Y   L   L   D   Y
T A S K   R E V E R S E S
```

144

```
V E R A C I T Y   O G L E
O   O   A   A   A   R   J
L E M U R   B E D S I D E
T   A   T   V   P   C
  A N N O U N C E M E N T
C   C   G   E   N     I
O N E   R I V E T   C O N
M   A   E   I   R   G
P E R S P I R A T I O N
O   O   H   I   O     A
S C A L E N E   O W N E D
E   R   R   V   U   E   D
D O S E   D E S S E R T S
```

145

```
R I F E   D A Y D R E A M
O   E   G   M   I X   E
L I M P O P O   S H I F T
L   U   L   E   A   T   A
E R R E D   B A P T I S M
R   E   A   P   N   O
C L I E N T   C O N G E R
O   S   E   R   I   P
A S S U A G E   N E I G H
S   U   G   C   T   M   O
T R I A L   E X E M P T S
E   N   E   D   D   L   I
R E G I S T E R   E Y E S
```

146

```
B O U L D E R S   F L E A
I   N   E   A   A   E   D
O N I O N   S A N C T U M
D   F   U   P   T   U   I
E N O U N C E   A S P E N
G   R   C   D   G   I
R E M A I N   L O N E R S
A   A   O   N   N   T
D U V E T   B U I L D E R
A   A   I   E   S   M   A
B A L C O N Y   T R O U T
L   U   N   E   I   S   O
E Y E D   E D U C A T O R
```

147

```
S U S P E N D S   S M O G
O   H   N   I   B   A   A
F L E E T   D R E D G E R
A   L   E   W   M   M   M
  O V E R E S T I M A T E
T   E   T   T   L       N
H A D   A H E A D   T O T
W   I   E   E   E   S
A W E I N S P I R I N G
R   X   I   M   A   I
T W I N N E D   E M B E R
E   S   G   I   N   L   I
D O T S   S P O T L E S S
```

148

```
P A R A S O L S   E P I C
R   E   U   O   F   E   R
A L T A R   N I R V A N A
C   I   P   E   E   R   F
T E N D R I L   U N L I T
I   U   I   Y   D       S
C R E A S E   W I S D O M
A   I   C   A   E   A
L U M E N   H A N D S O N
J   A   G   I   S   P   S
O C C U L T S   L O A T H
K   H   Y   E   I   I   I
E R O S   C L A P T R A P
```

SOLUTIONS

149

```
A L A C R I T Y   P R I M
N   L   E   A   B E   I
T I L L S   C H I S E L S
I   O   U   T   O D   C
H E W E R   I   G   S H E
I   E   R E C U R     L
S   D   E       A R   L
T     C H I M P   I   A
A I L   T   N   H A V E N
M   I   I   T   I U   E
I R K S O M E   C E L L O
N   E   N   R   A E   E
E D D Y   I N F L A T E S
```

150

```
I T C H   O C C U R R E D
D   O   P   O   N E   I
I M P O U N D   C L A W S
O   S   R   D   H C   A
S L E E P   L E A S H E D
Y   O   E   R   R E   V
N I C E S T   F I E S T A
C   A   E   S   T   N
R E S T F U L   A D A P T
A   H   U   O   B D   A
T W I L L   G A L L I N G
I   E   L   A   E E   E
C A R R Y I N G   F U N D
```

151

```
U N T E S T E D   S W I M
N   A   U   X   C H   A
A D L I B   P R O W E S S
C   E   S   E   N S   S
C O N I C A L   V O L G A
O   T   R   S   E   C
M Y S T I C   S N A T C H
P   P   T   R   U
A L L O T   U N I F I E S
N   O   I   R   O G   E
I N D O O R S   N I G H T
E   G   N   U   A E   T
D U E S   D E C L A R E S
```

152

```
T A M P   E M P H A S I S
R   O   M   O   I E   U
A B R E A S T   N I C E R
N   A   T   O   D T   R
S Y L P H   R E Q U I R E
G   G   E   S   U O   P
R E A L M S   C A N N O T
E   R   A   C   R R
S C R A T C H   T A U N T
S   A   I   O   E N   I
I O N I C   S I R O C C O
O   G   A   E   S L   U
N E E D L I N G   P E G S
```

153

```
S C H E M I N G   I D O L
E   A   A   O   F   O   I
M E L O N   U N I T I N G
I   T   U   G   E   N   H
C L I F F   A   L   G U T
O   N   G   A C T E D   F
N   G   C   C     G W   I
S       T O W E L   R   N
C O W   U   O   A M O N G
I   I   O   R   S   N   E
O P P R E S S   S U G A R
U   E   R   E   E   E   E
S O D A   O N E S I D E D
```

154

```
B A W L   P E R S I S T S
E   I   C   L   T   C   E
A N D R O I D   U S U A L
S   E   N   E   P   D   F
T E N E T   S L E N D E R
O   R   T   F   E   I    
F I S C A L   L A P D O G
B   W   D   P   C       H
U N A L I K E   T H E F T
R   L   C   A   I   X   E
D E L F T   C H O R I Z O
E   O   E   H   N   L   U
N O W A D A Y S   B E E S
```

155

```
C R O T C H E T   R U I N
O   D   O   R   E   N   O
R A D O N   M I L L I O N
R   M   G   I   E   T   A
O V E R R A N   C H E A P
B   N   E   E   T       P
O U T A G E   C R E C H E
R       A   L O O   A    
A N G S T   E M P E R O R
T   A   I   S   L   D   A
I M P I O U S   A L I E N
O   E   N   O   T   A   C
N O D E   U N D E R L I E
```

156

```
U G L Y   G O O D N E S S
N   A   O   R   I   V   T
C A N A S T A   S T A T E
O   K   T   L   I   C   A
M A Y B E   L A N G U I D
F       N   Y   E   F    
O R B I T S   G E N E V A
R   E   A   U   C   S    
T I G H T E N   T A I N T
A   O   I   I   A   B   N
B O N G O   S U N R I S E
L   I   U   O   T   Z   S
E L A P S I N G   S A P S
```

SOLUTIONS

157

```
S U R V I V A L   A L G A
O E   N   R   I   A   N
C U B I C   M I N U T I A
K   O   O   A   D   I   L
  C U R M U D G E O N L Y
S   N   P   A   F     T
N U D G E S   G E M I N I
A     T   B   N   N   C
P R E R E Q U I S I T E
S   D   N   T   I   R   S
H A I R C U T   B L U R T
O   C   Y   E   L   D   A
T U T U   G R E E N E R Y
```

158

```
S L A L O M   V   W   A
U   D   E M I G R A N T
G A D   A   O   I   G
A   L I N T E L   G O L D
R   E   S   E   G   E
Y O D E L   E N G L I S H
    M   B   T     E
D E D U C E S   P S A L M
  N   L   D   M   V   A
L A V A   T W I N G E   M
  C   T   I   C   R A M A
S T R E A M E R   S   A
  S   D   E   O R D E A L
```

159

```
N O S E D I V E   P L E A
I   E   I   A   D   E   L
P A N I C   C H E R V I L
S   S   T   A   S   E   A
  R O M A N T I C A L L Y
L   R   T   E   R     I
U P S H O T   G I B B O N
M   R   G   P   O   G
I N D I S C R E T I O N
N   W   H   E   I   T   O
O N E T I M E   O D I U M
U   L   P   D   N   N   I
S O L D   E Y E S I G H T
```

160

```
P E R M   P R O L I F I C
H   O   D   E   E   L   U
I M P L I E D   G A U N T
L   E   S   U   I   V   T
A S S E T   C A T F I S H
N   I   E   I   A   E
T I R I N G   E M B L E M
H   O   C   F   A     U
R I S O T T O   T O L L S
O   T   N   R   E   A   T
P U R S E   M A L A R I A
I   U   S   A   Y   C   R
C A M P S I T E   C H A D
```